Based on the best-selling keyboard method *by K*

THE COMPLE
KEYBOARD PLA

15 ALL-TIME FAVOURITES

Wise Publications
part of The Music Sales Group
London/New York/Paris/Sydney/Copenhagen/Berlin/Madrid/Tokyo

Published by
Wise Publications
8/9 Frith Street, London W1D 3JB, UK

Exclusive Distributors:
Music Sales Limited
8/9 Frith Street, London W1D 3JB, UK.
Music Sales Pty Limited
120 Rothschild Avenue, Rosebery, NSW 2018, Australia.

Order No. AM984203
ISBN 1-84609-281-7

Compiled by Nick Crispin.
Music arranged by Paul Honey.
Music processed by Paul Ewers Music Design.
Cover photos (Nat 'King' Cole & Dean Martin) courtesy of Redferns.
Printed in the EU.

Beyond The Sea *Bobby Darin* **6**
Blueberry Hill *Fats Domino* **8**
Can't Take My Eyes Off You *Andy Williams* **10**
Crazy *Patsy Cline* **12**
It's Not Unusual *Tom Jones* **14**
It's Now Or Never *Elvis Presley* **20**
Magic Moments *Perry Como* **22**
Mona Lisa *Nat 'King' Cole* **24**
Ring Of Fire *Johnny Cash* **26**
Runaway *Del Shannon* **17**
Telstar *The Tornados* **28**
That's Amoré *Dean Martin* **30**
Walk On By *Dionne Warwick* **33**
What A Wonderful World *Louis Armstrong* **38**
Wichita Lineman *Glen Campbell* **36**

Chord Charts **4, 5**

Master Chord Chart

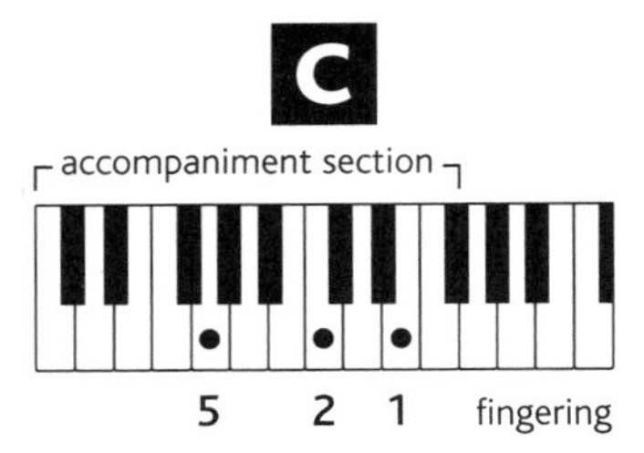
C
accompaniment section
5 2 1 fingering

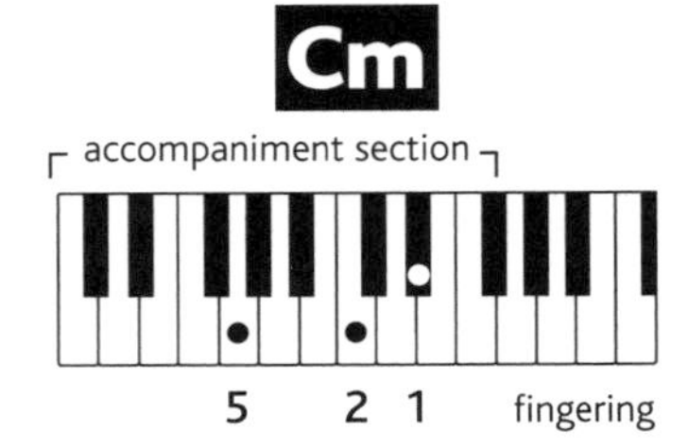
Cm
accompaniment section
5 2 1 fingering

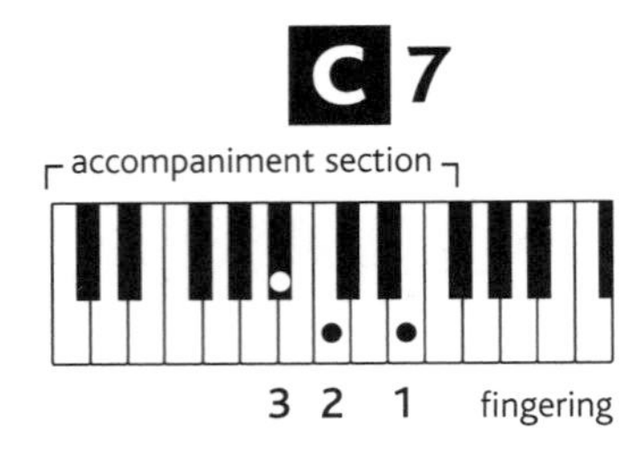
C7
accompaniment section
3 2 1 fingering

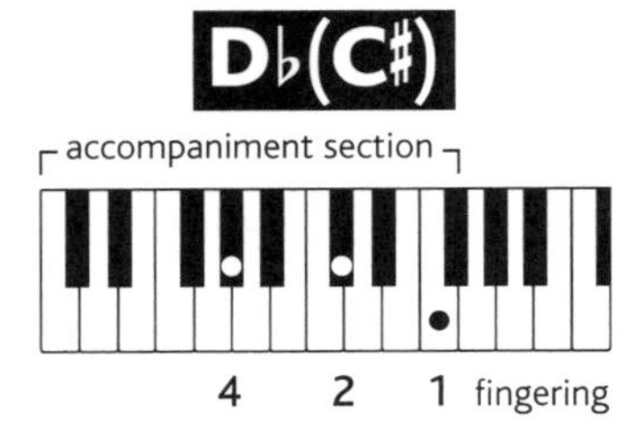
D♭(C♯)
accompaniment section
4 2 1 fingering

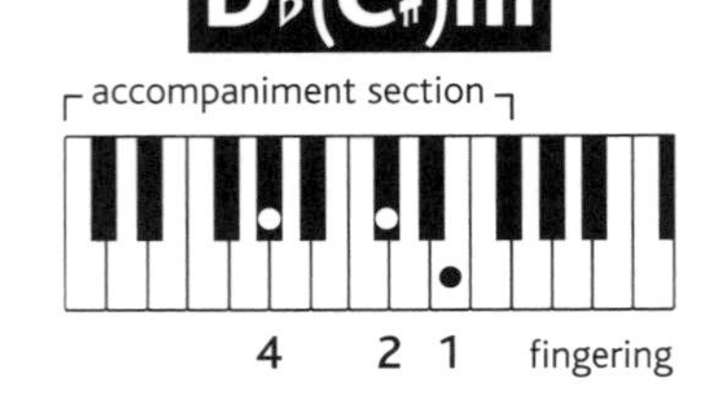
D♭(C♯)m
accompaniment section
4 2 1 fingering

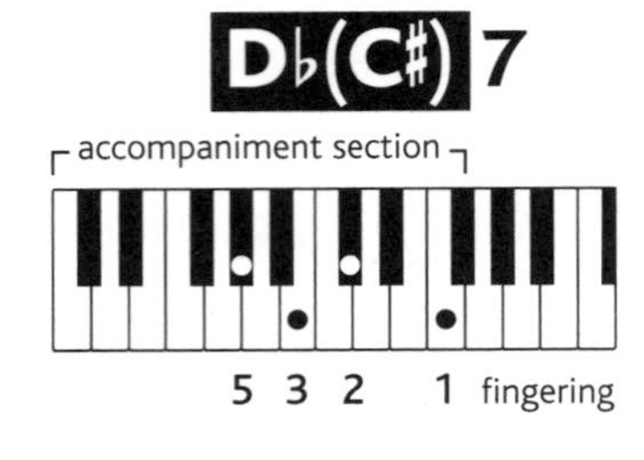
D♭(C♯)7
accompaniment section
5 3 2 1 fingering

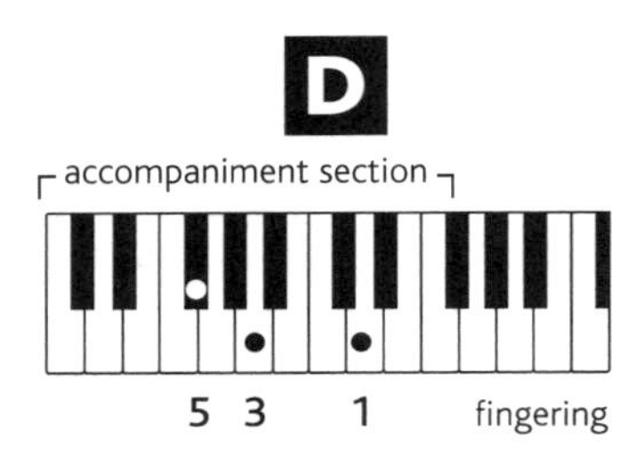
D
accompaniment section
5 3 1 fingering

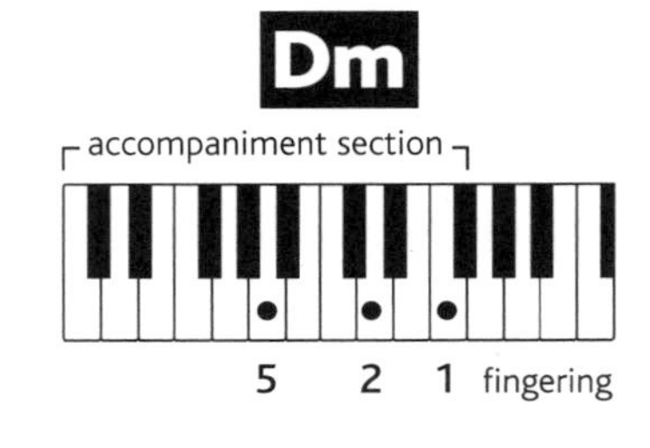
Dm
accompaniment section
5 2 1 fingering

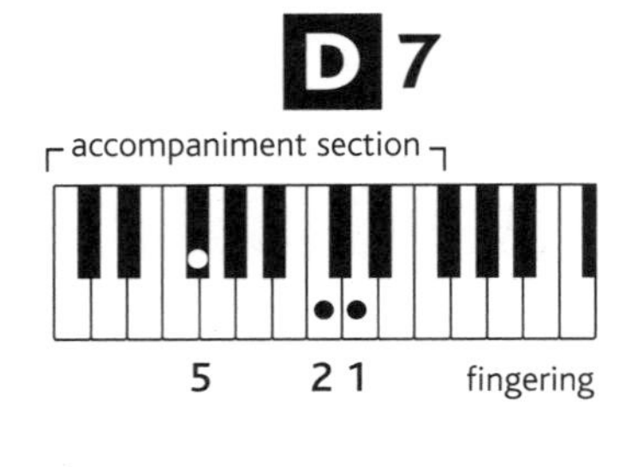
D7
accompaniment section
5 2 1 fingering

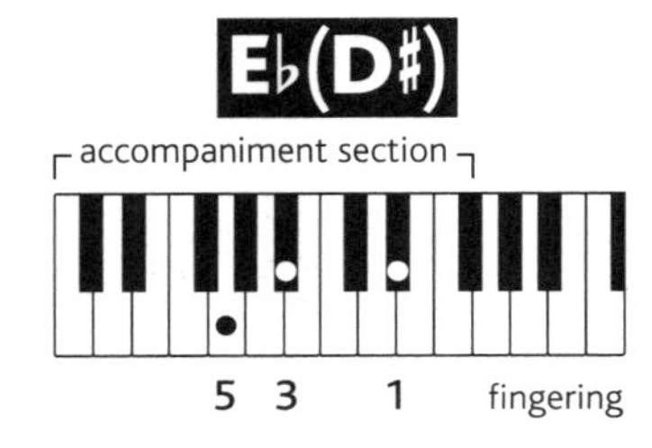
E♭(D♯)
accompaniment section
5 3 1 fingering

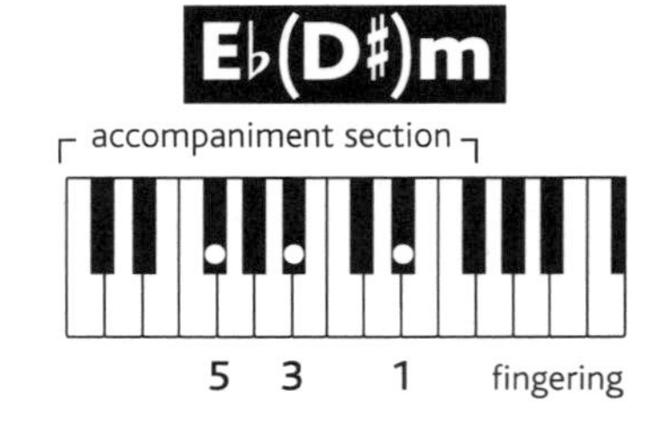
E♭(D♯)m
accompaniment section
5 3 1 fingering

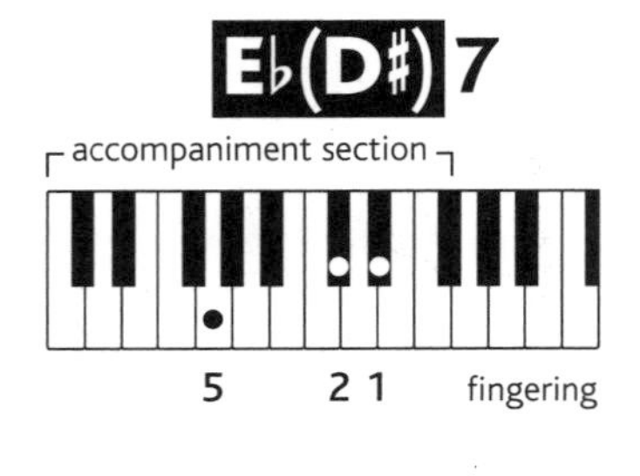
E♭(D♯)7
accompaniment section
5 2 1 fingering

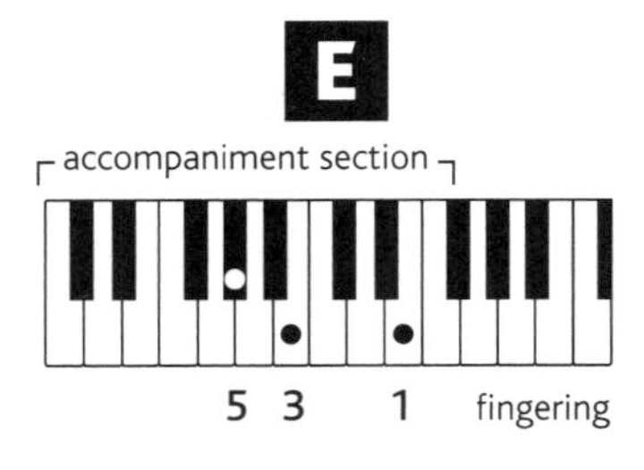
E
accompaniment section
5 3 1 fingering

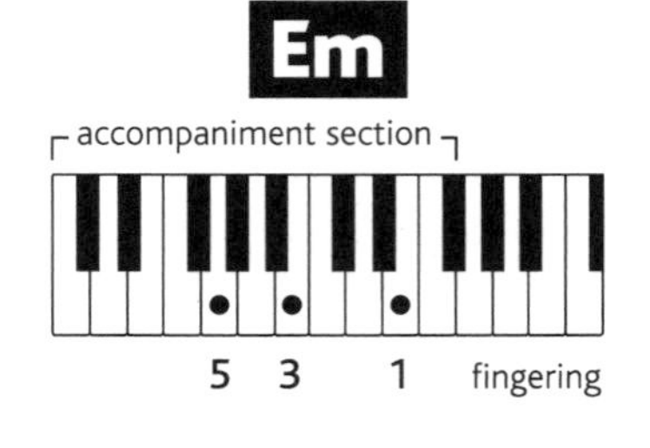
Em
accompaniment section
5 3 1 fingering

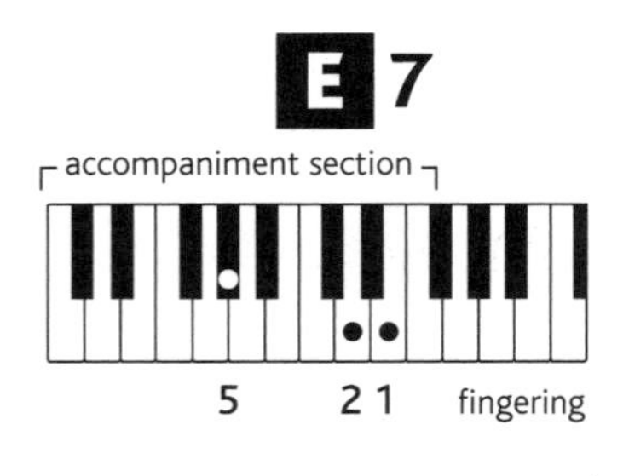
E7
accompaniment section
5 2 1 fingering

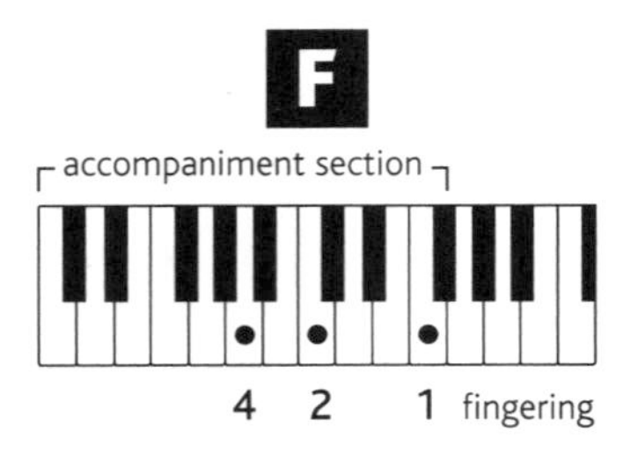
F
accompaniment section
4 2 1 fingering

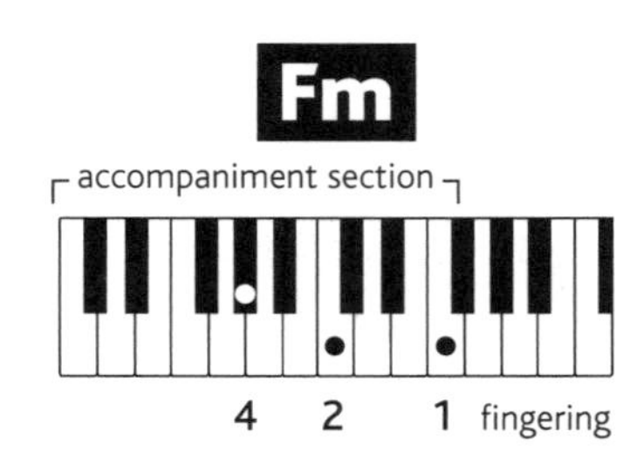
Fm
accompaniment section
4 2 1 fingering

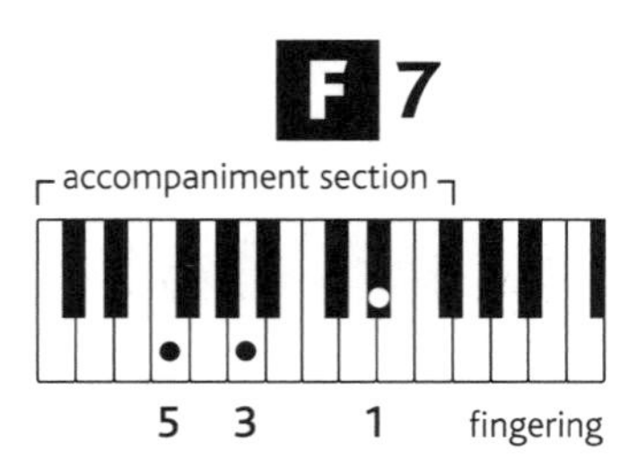
F7
accompaniment section
5 3 1 fingering

Master Chord Chart

accompaniment section

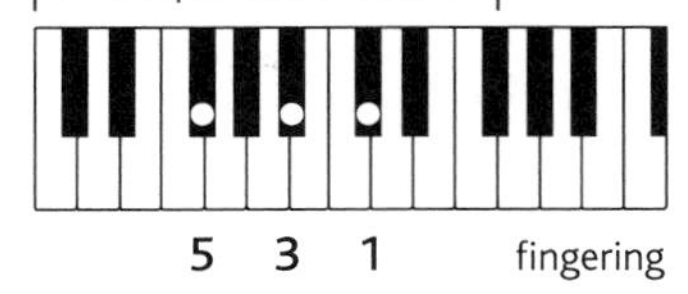

5 3 1 fingering

G♭(F♯)m

accompaniment section

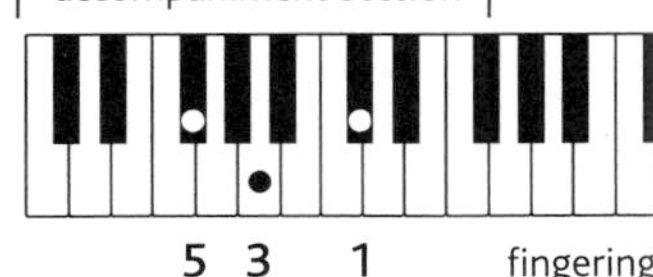

5 3 1 fingering

G♭(F♯)7

accompaniment section

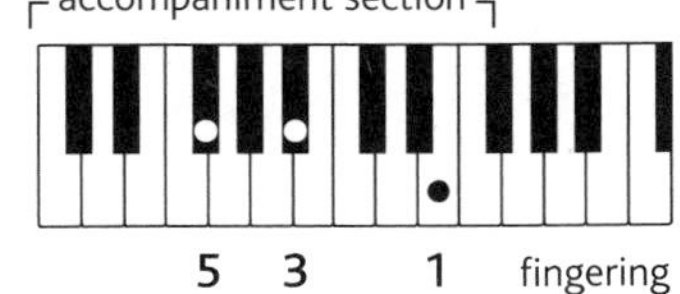

5 3 1 fingering

G

accompaniment section

5 3 1 fingering

Gm

accompaniment section

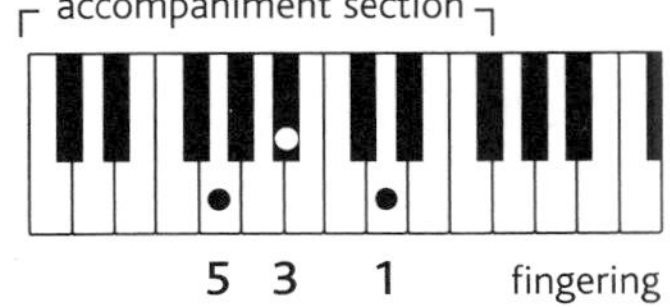

5 3 1 fingering

G7

accompaniment section

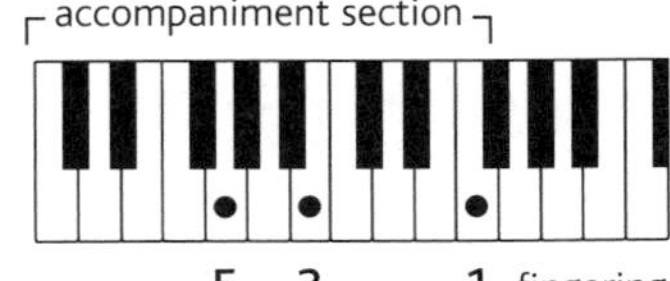

5 3 1 fingering

A♭(G♯)

accompaniment section

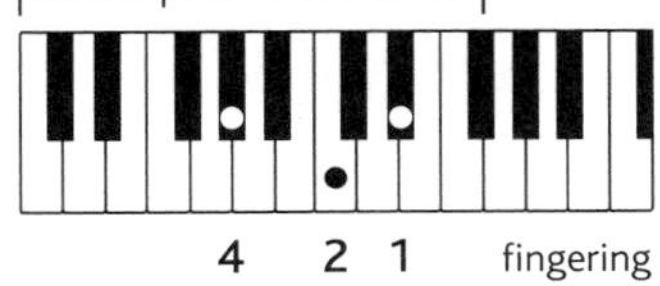

4 2 1 fingering

A♭(G♯)m

accompaniment section

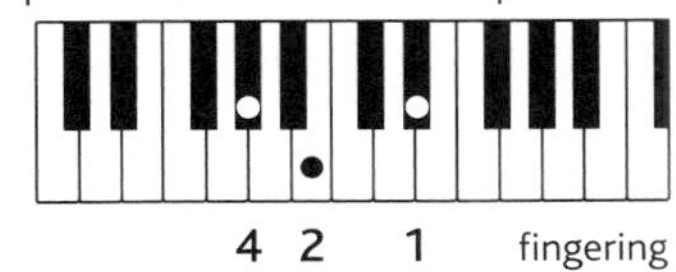

4 2 1 fingering

accompaniment section

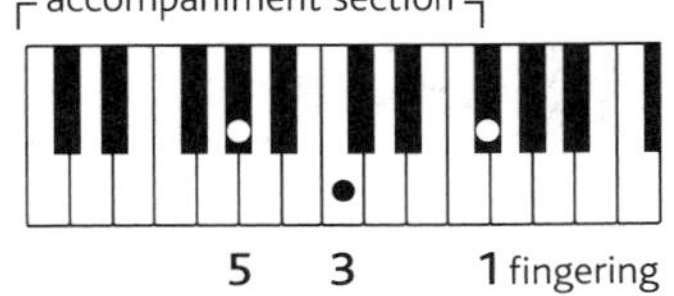

5 3 1 fingering

A

accompaniment section

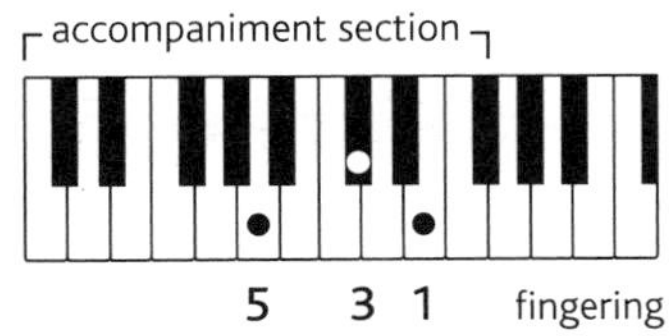

5 3 1 fingering

accompaniment section

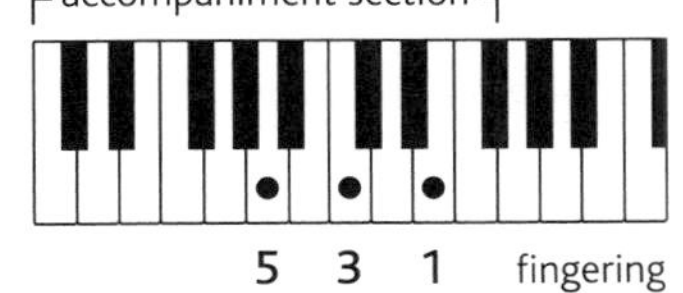

5 3 1 fingering

accompaniment section

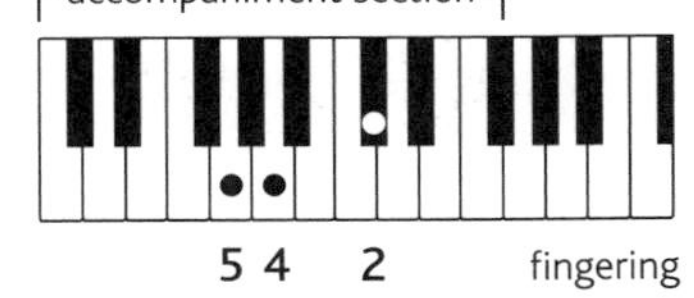

5 4 2 fingering

B♭

accompaniment section

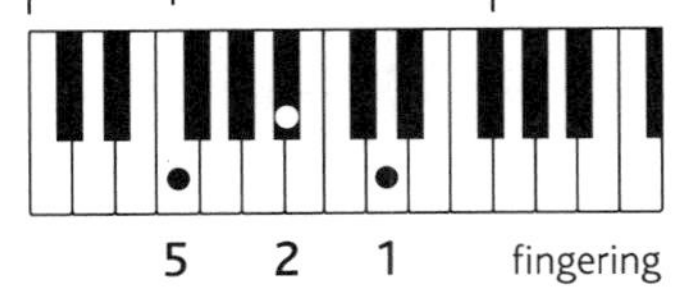

5 2 1 fingering

B♭m

accompaniment section

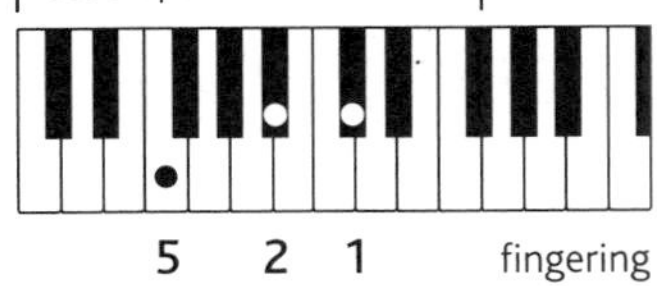

5 2 1 fingering

B♭7

accompaniment section

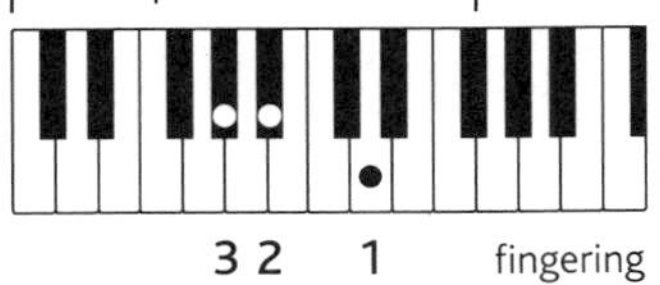

3 2 1 fingering

B

accompaniment section

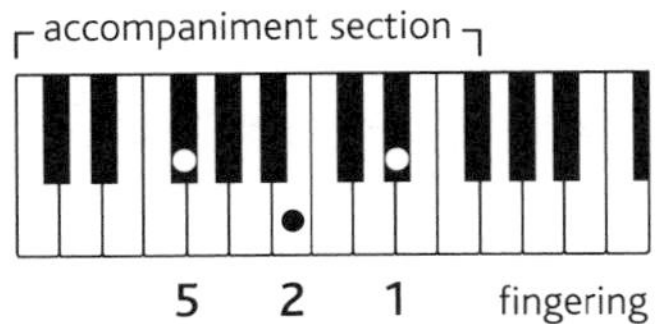

5 2 1 fingering

Bm

accompaniment section

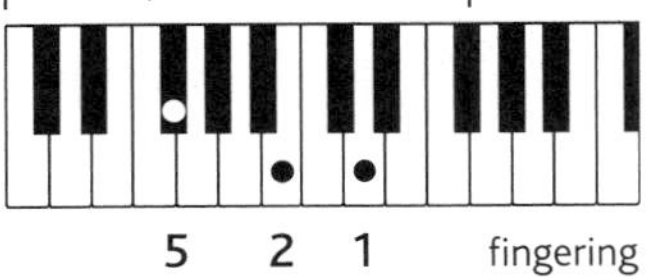

5 2 1 fingering

B7

accompaniment section

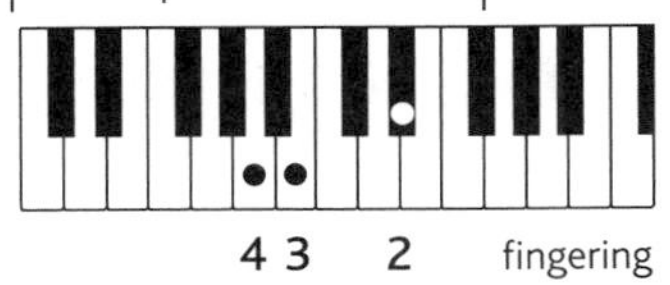

4 3 2 fingering

Beyond The Sea

Original Words & Music by Charles Trenet
English Words by Jack Lawrence

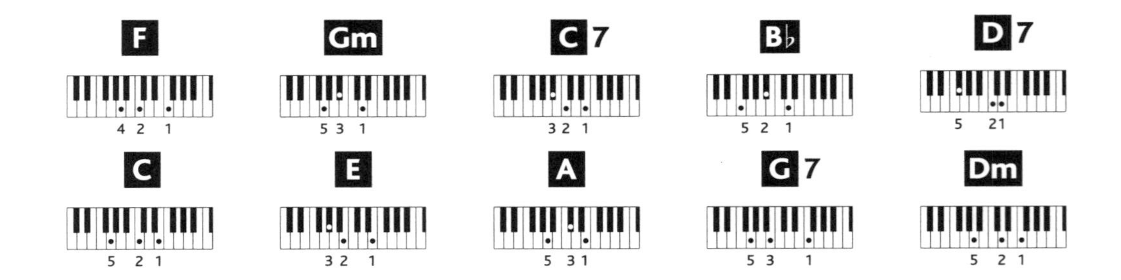

F
4 2 1
Gm
5 3 1
C7
3 2 1
B♭
5 2 1
D7
5 21
C
5 2 1
E
3 2 1
A
5 3 1
G7
5 3 1
Dm
5 2 1

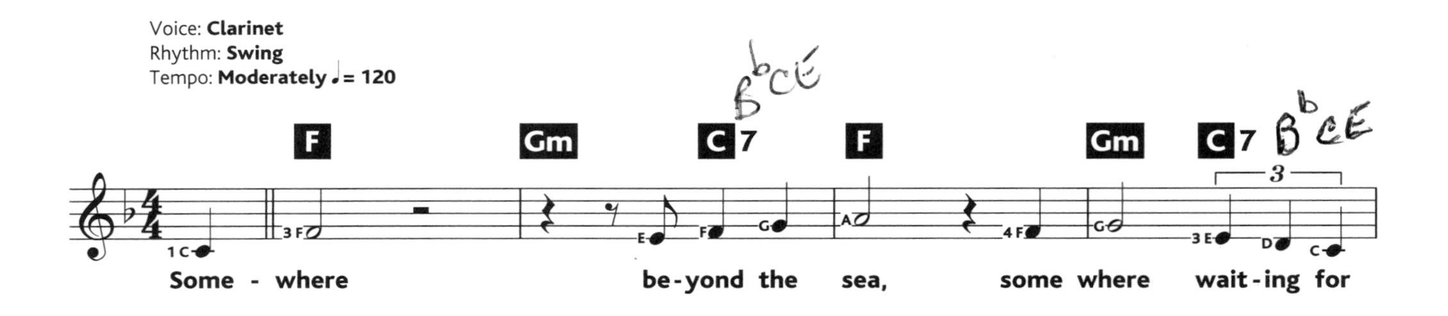

Voice: **Clarinet**
Rhythm: **Swing**
Tempo: **Moderately** ♩= 120
F Gm C7 F Gm C7
Some - where be-yond the sea, some where wait-ing for

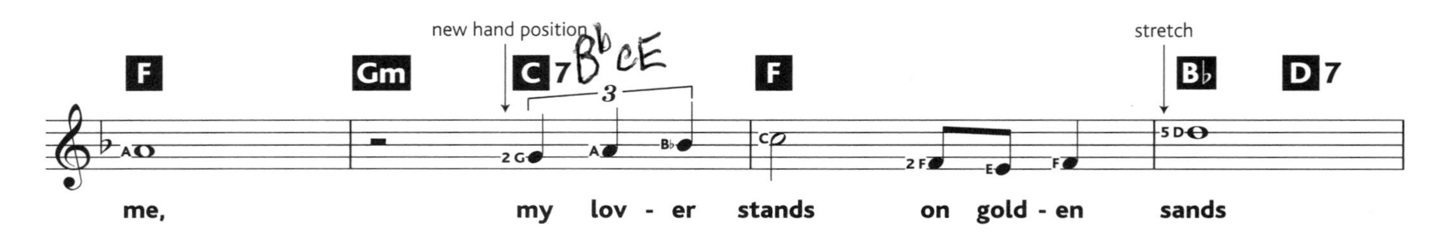

new hand position
stretch
F Gm C7 F B♭ D7
me, my lov - er stands on gold - en sands

3rd finger over

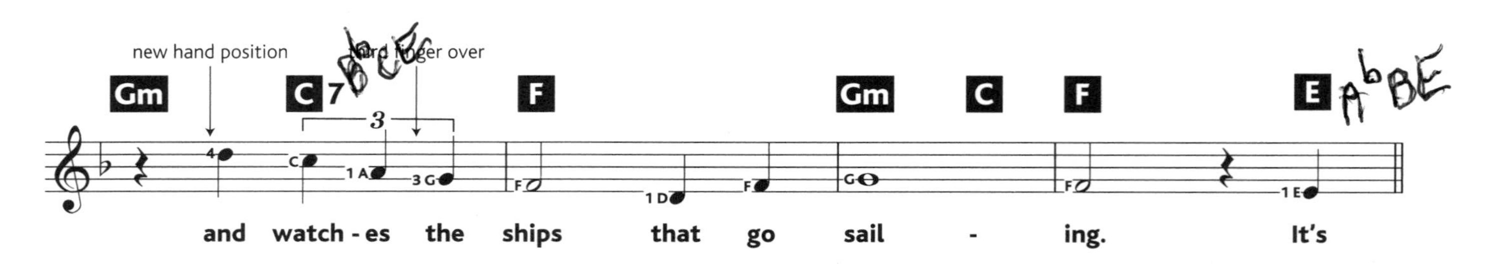

new hand position
3rd finger over
Gm C7 F Gm C F E
and watch - es the ships that go sail - ing. It's

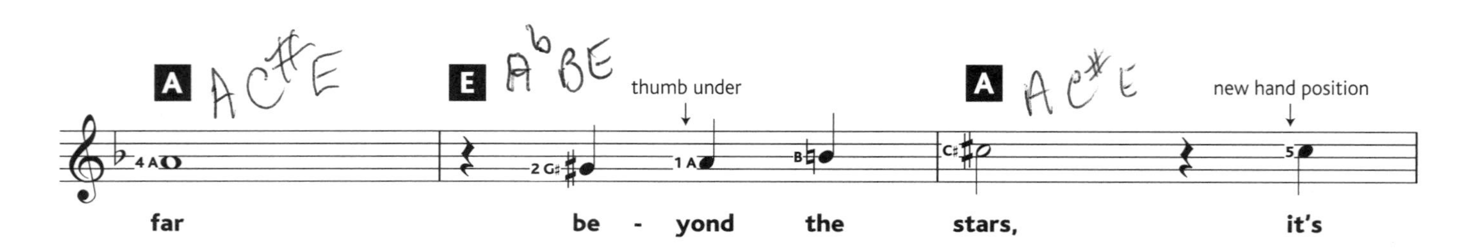

thumb under
new hand position
A E A
far be - yond the stars, it's

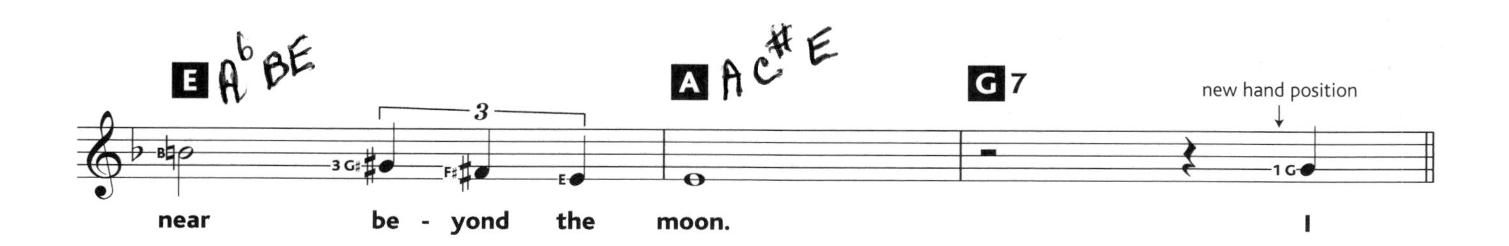
E
A
G7
new hand position
near be - yond the moon. I

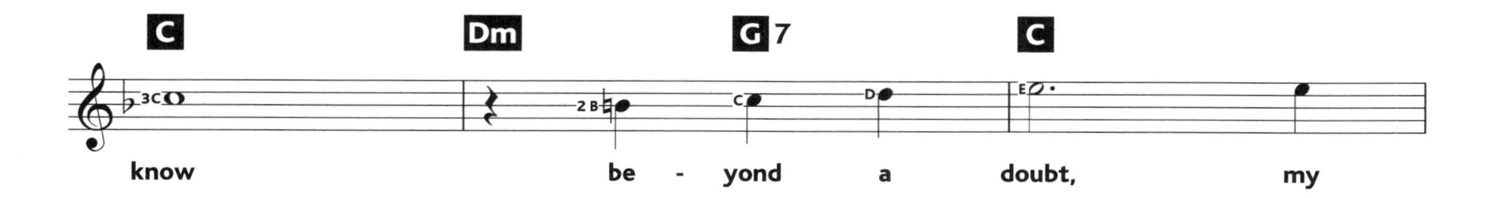
C
Dm
G7
C
know be - yond a doubt, my

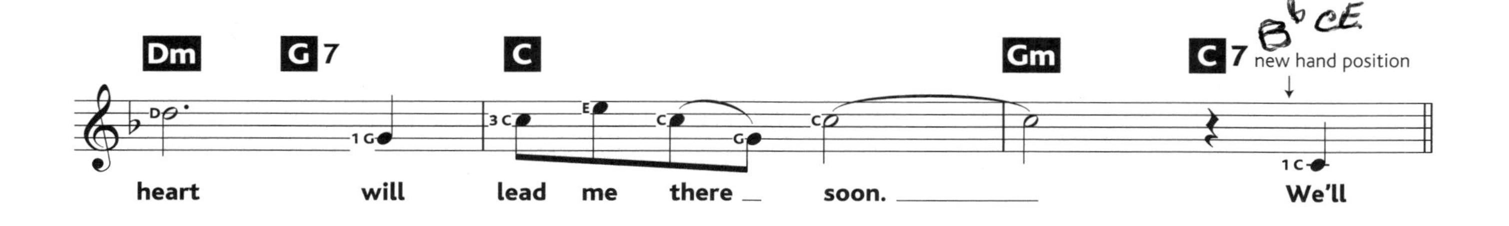
Dm
G7
C
Gm
C7
new hand position
heart will lead me there soon. We'll

F
Gm
C7
F
Gm
C7
meet be-yond the shore, we'll kiss just like be -

F
Gm
new hand position
C7
F
B♭
- fore. Hap - py we'll be be - yond the sea,

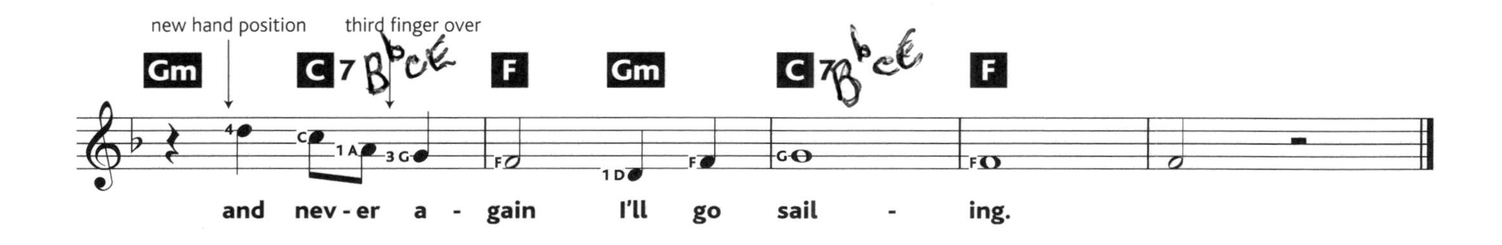
new hand position
third finger over
Gm
C7
F
Gm
C7
F
and nev - er a - gain I'll go sail - ing.

Blueberry Hill

Words & Music by Larry Stock, Al Lewis & Vincent Rose

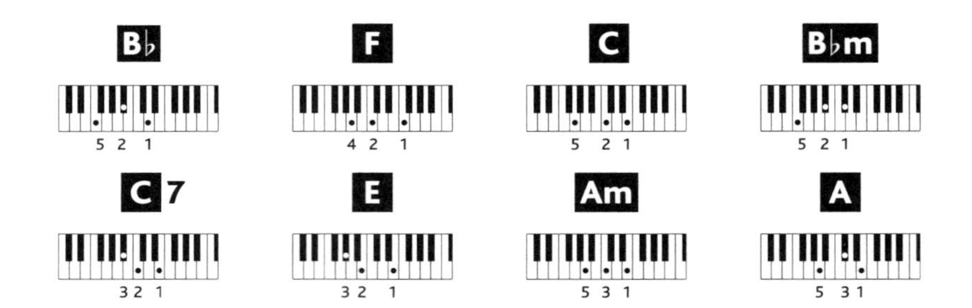

B♭
5 2 1
F
4 2 1
C
5 2 1
B♭m
5 2 1
C7
3 2 1
E
3 2 1
Am
5 3 1
A
5 3 1

Voice: **Piano**
Rhythm: **Rock 'n' Roll**
Tempo: **Moderately** ♩. = 90

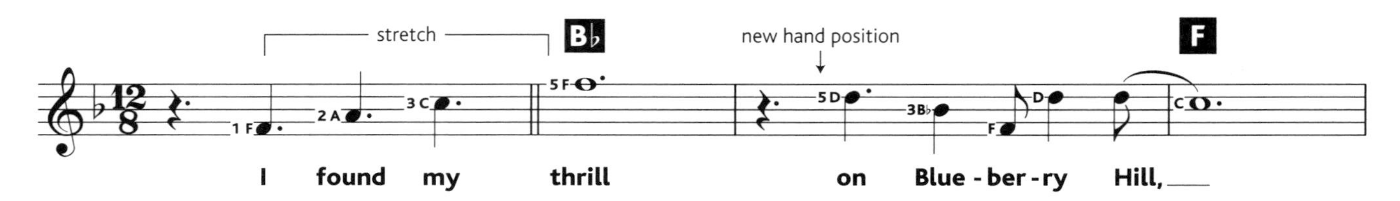

stretch
B♭
new hand position
F
I found my thrill on Blue - ber - ry Hill,

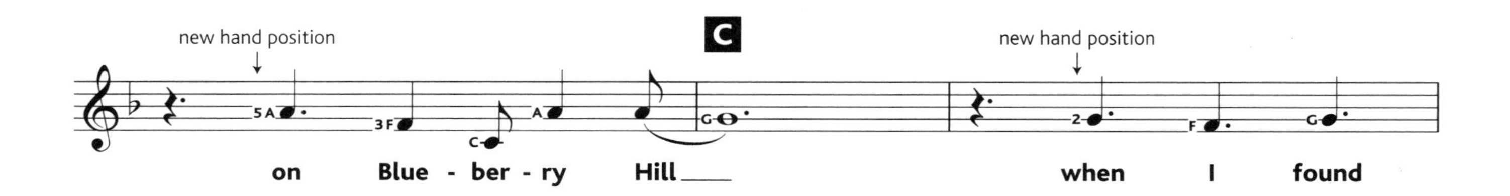

new hand position
C
new hand position
on Blue - ber - ry Hill when I found

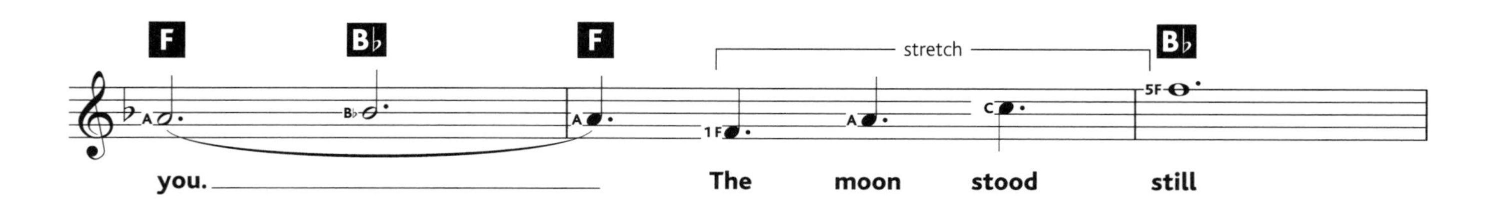

F
B♭
F
stretch
B♭
you. The moon stood still

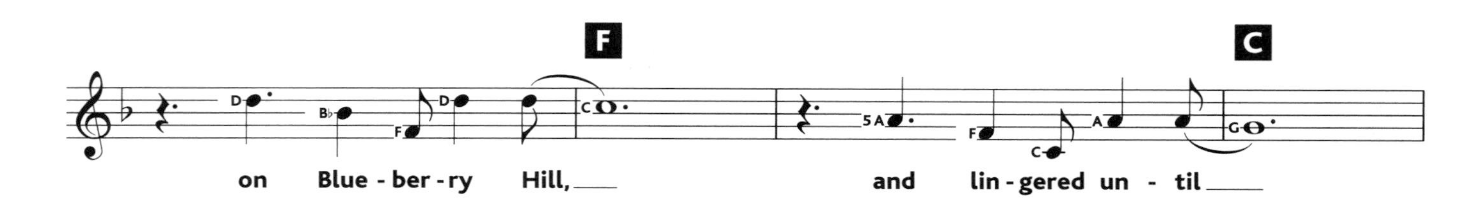

F
C
on Blue - ber - ry Hill, and lin - gered un - til

F B♭m F C7
new hand position
my dreams came true. The wind in the

C7 F
wil - low played love's sweet me - lo - dy,

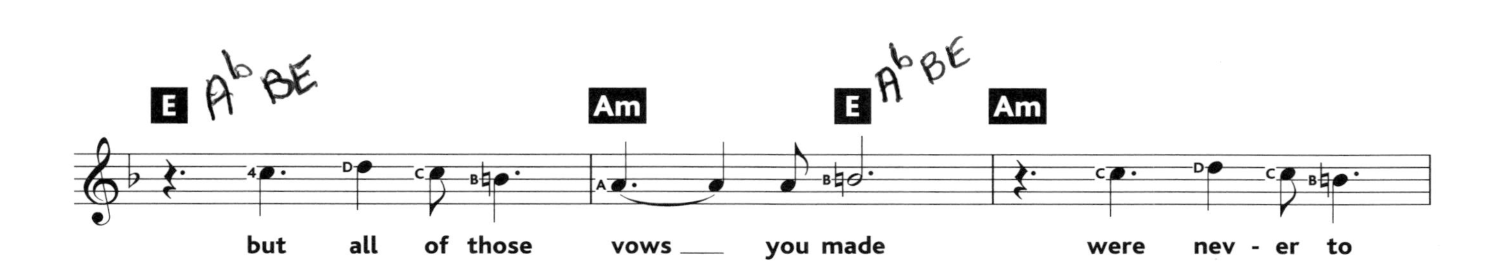
E Am E Am
but all of those vows ___ you made were nev - er to

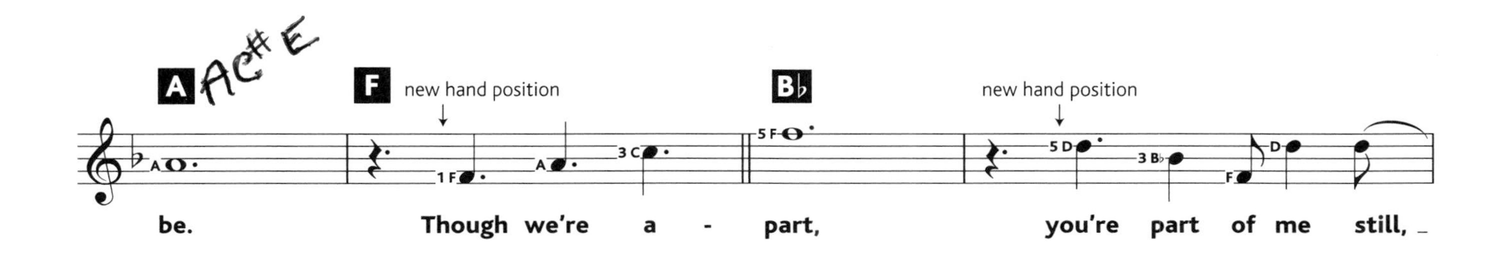
A F B♭
new hand position
new hand position
be. Though we're a - part, you're part of me still, _

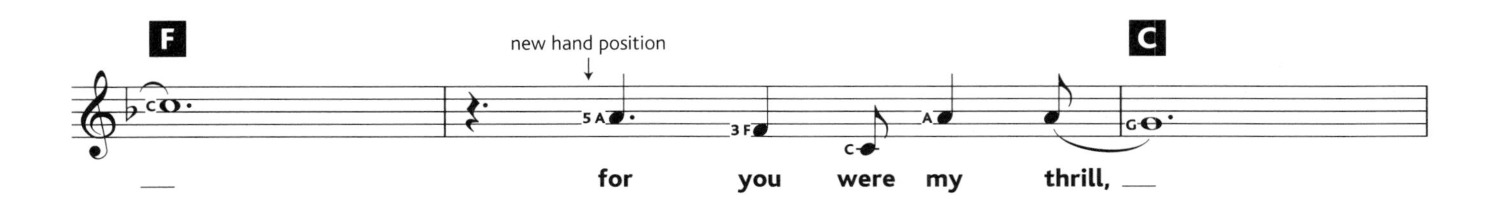
F C
new hand position
___ for you were my thrill, ___

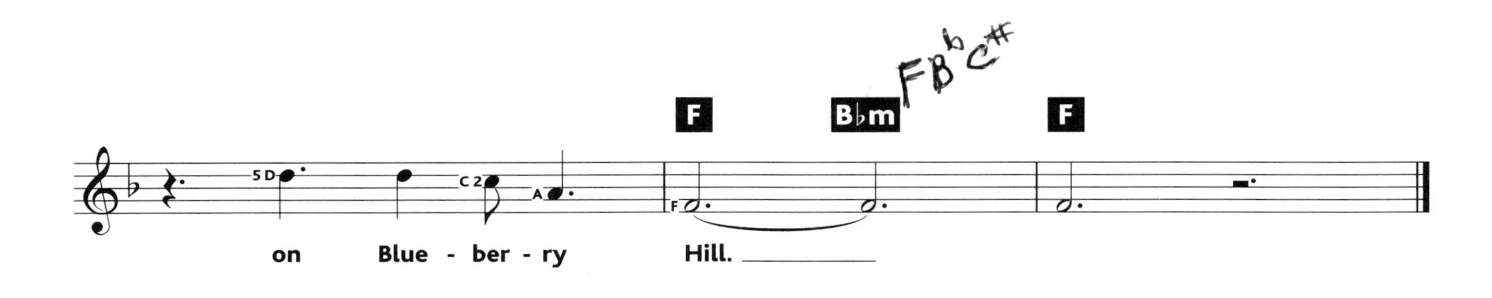
F B♭m F
on Blue - ber - ry Hill. ________

Can't Take My Eyes Off You

Words & Music by Bob Crewe & Bob Gaudio

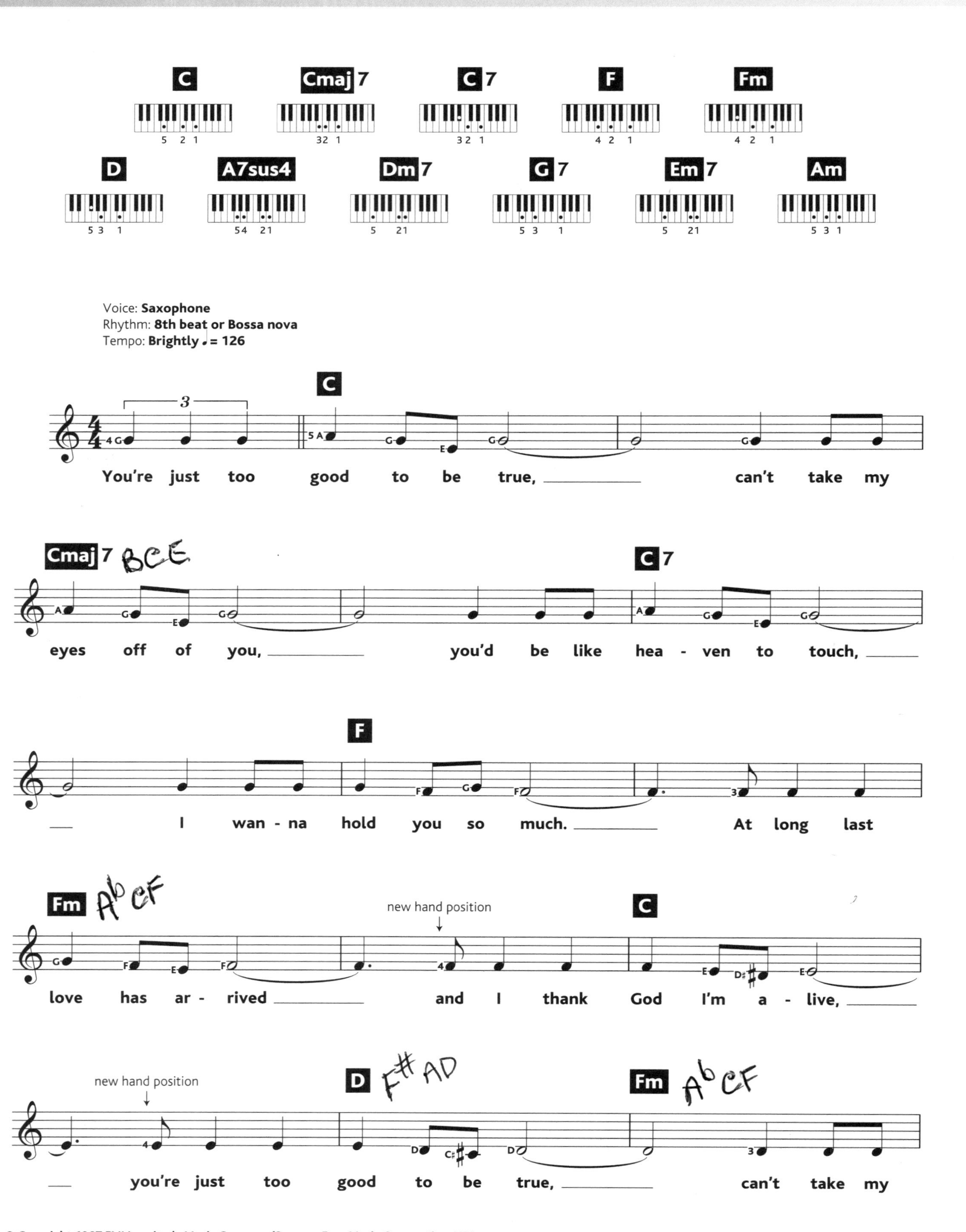

C
Cmaj7
C7
F
Fm
D
A7sus4
Dm7
G7
Em7
Am
Voice: Saxophone
Rhythm: 8th beat or Bossa nova
Tempo: Brightly ♩ = 126
You're just too good to be true, can't take my
eyes off of you, you'd be like hea - ven to touch,
I wan - na hold you so much. At long last
love has ar - rived and I thank God I'm a - live,
new hand position
you're just too good to be true, can't take my

C
stretch
A7sus4 GADE
Dm7
eyes off of you. I love you ba - by and if it's

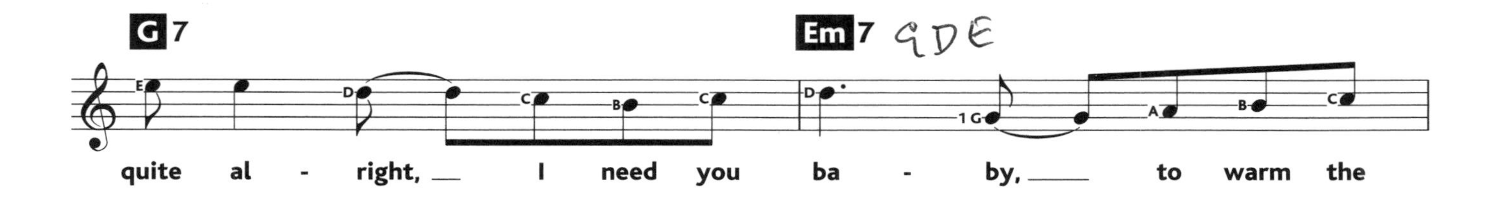
G7
Em7 GDE
quite al - right, I need you ba - by, to warm the

Am
Dm7
G7
lone - ly night, I love you ba - by, trust in me when I

Cmaj7 BCE
stretch
A7sus4 GADE
Dm7
say, oh pret - ty ba - by, don't bring me

G7
Em7 GDE
Am
down I pray, oh pret - ty ba - by now that I've found you, stay and let me

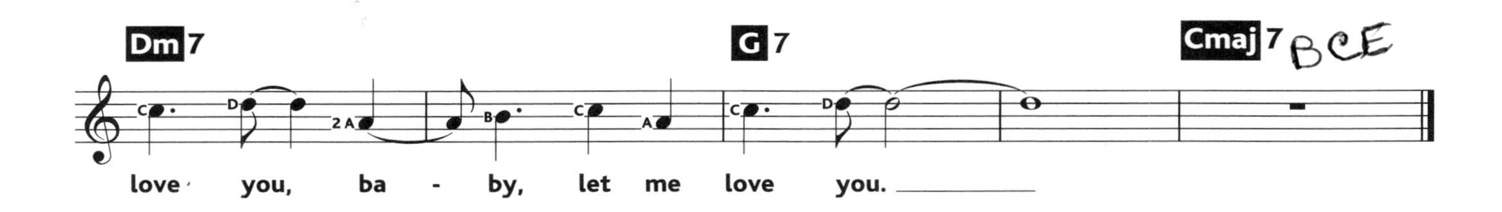
Dm7
G7
Cmaj7 BCE
love you, ba - by, let me love you.

Crazy

Words & Music by Willie Nelson

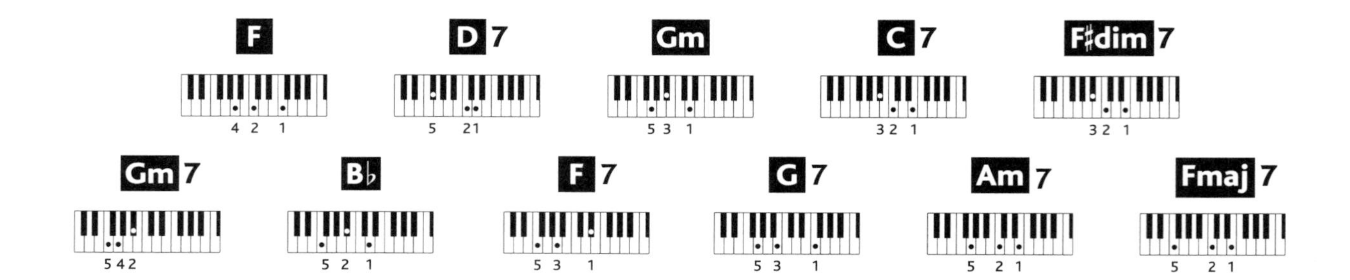
F
D7
Gm
C7
F♯dim7
Gm7
B♭
F7
G7
Am7
Fmaj7

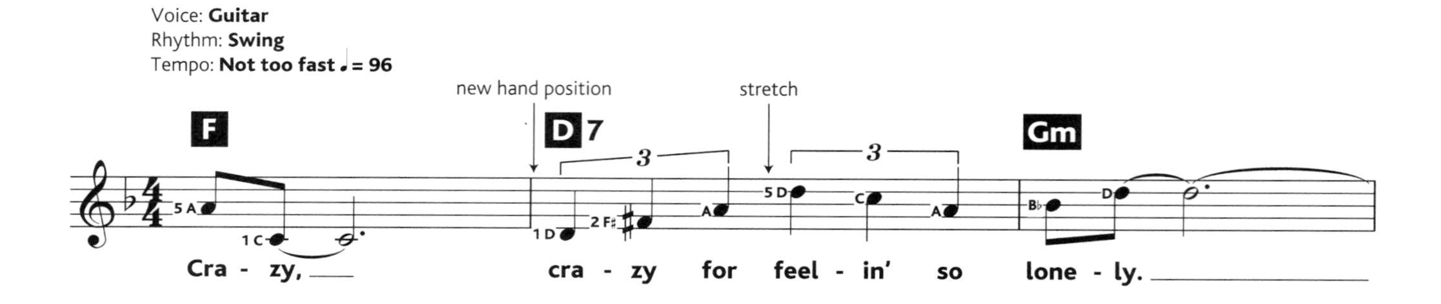
Voice: Guitar
Rhythm: Swing
Tempo: Not too fast ♩ = 96
new hand position
stretch
F
D7
Gm
Cra - zy,
cra - zy for feel - in' so lone - ly.

C7
stretch
stretch
I'm cra - zy,
cra - zy for feel - in' so

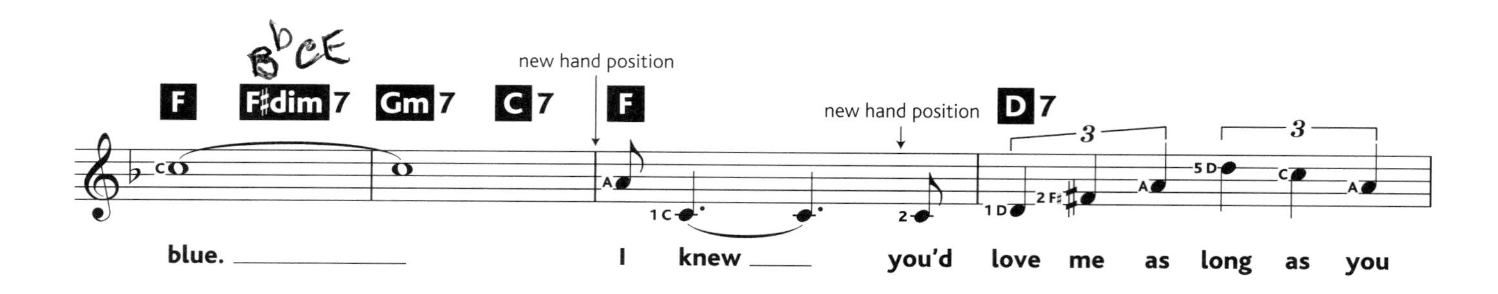
F F♯dim7 Gm7 C7 F D7
new hand position
new hand position
blue.
I knew you'd love me as long as you

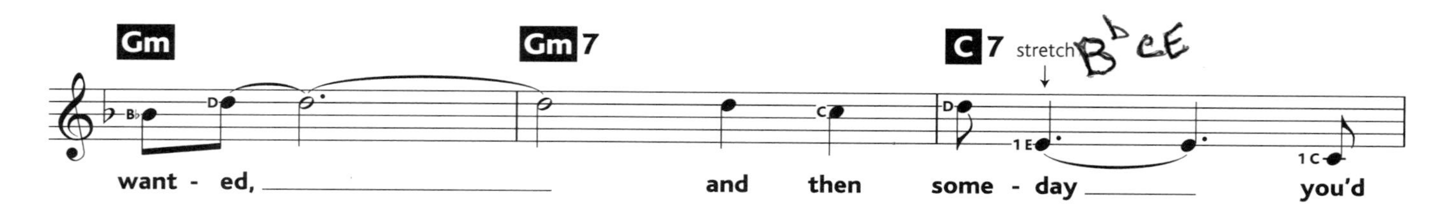
Gm Gm7 C7
stretch
want - ed, and then some - day you'd

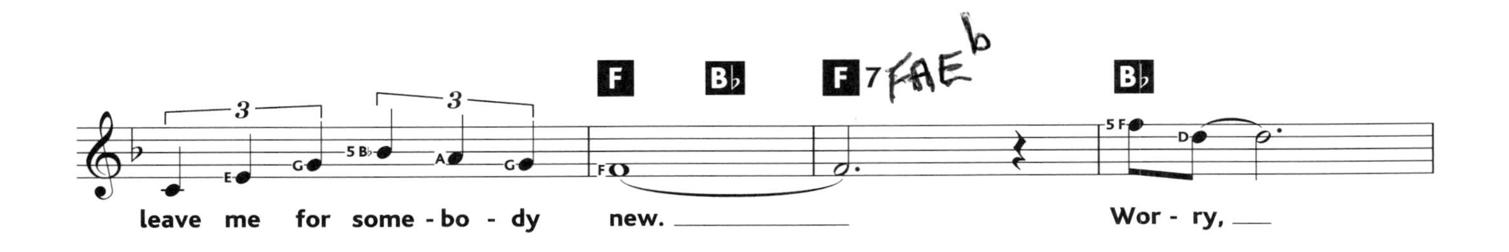
F Bb F7 Bb
leave me for some - bo - dy new. Wor - ry,

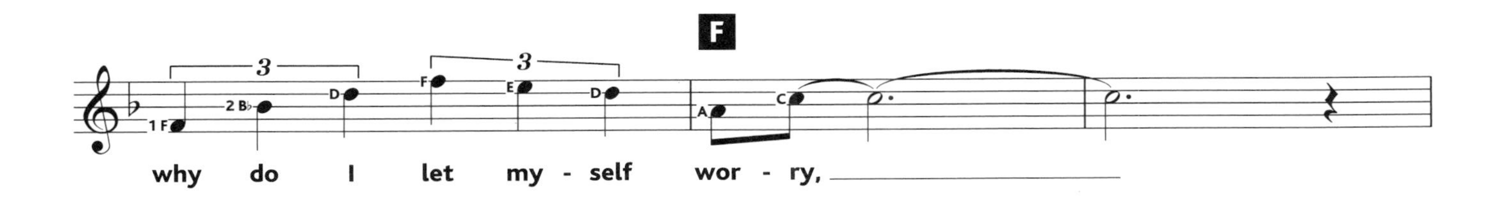
F
why do I let my - self wor - ry,

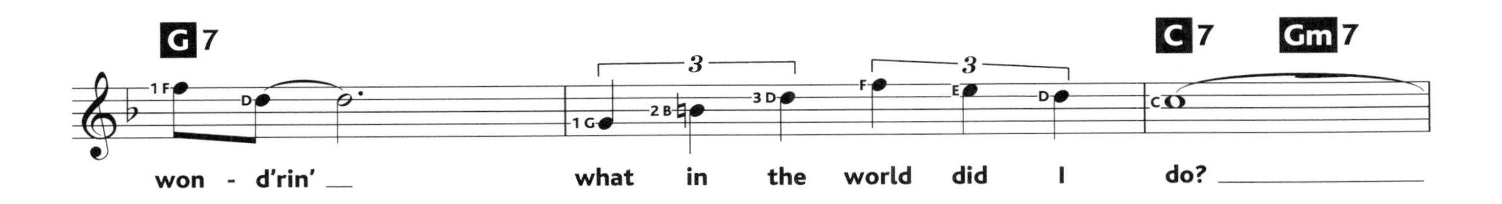
G7 C7 Gm7
won - d'rin' what in the world did I do?

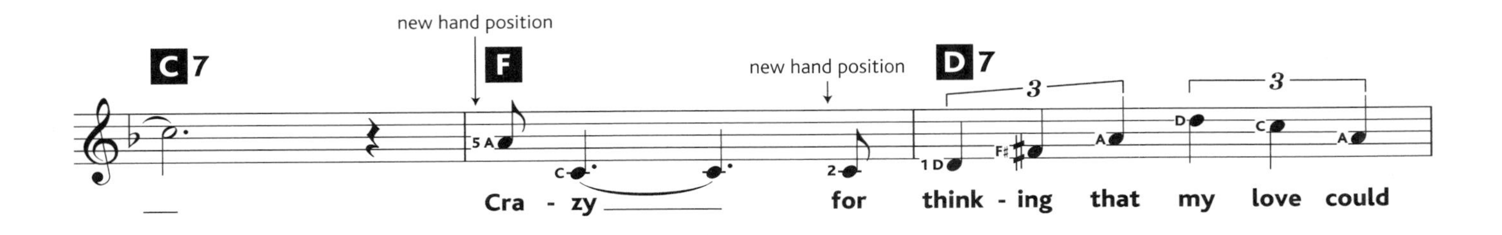
new hand position
C7 F D7
new hand position
Cra - zy for think - ing that my love could

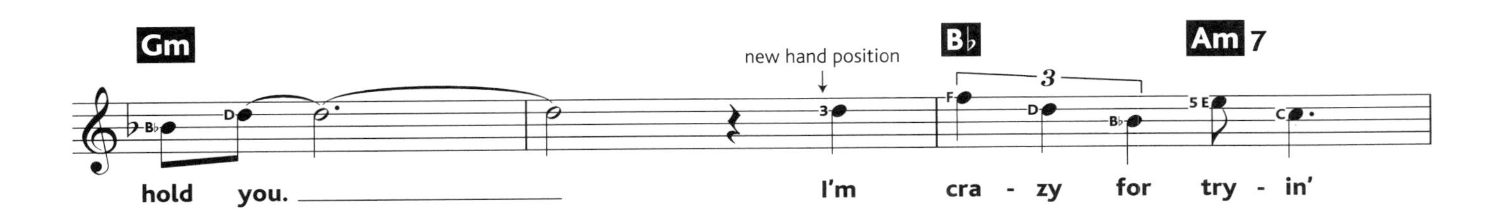
Gm Bb Am7
new hand position
hold you. I'm cra - zy for try - in'

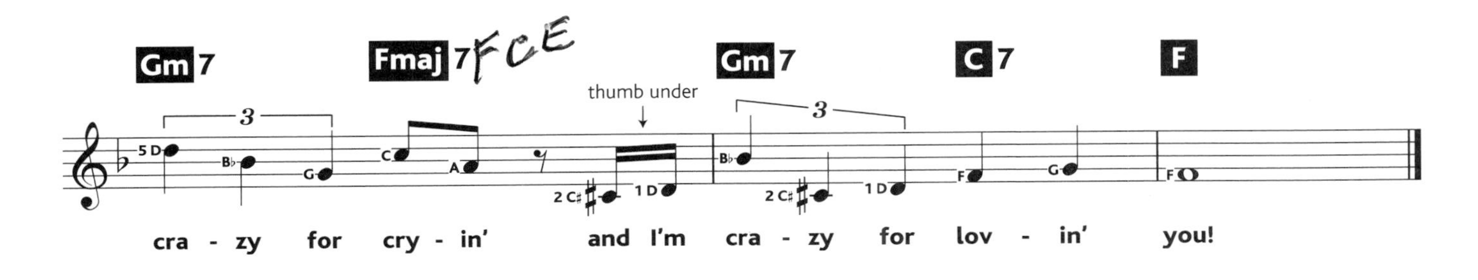
Gm7 Fmaj7 Gm7 C7 F
thumb under
cra - zy for cry - in' and I'm cra - zy for lov - in' you!

It's Not Unusual

Words & Music by Gordon Mills & Les Reed

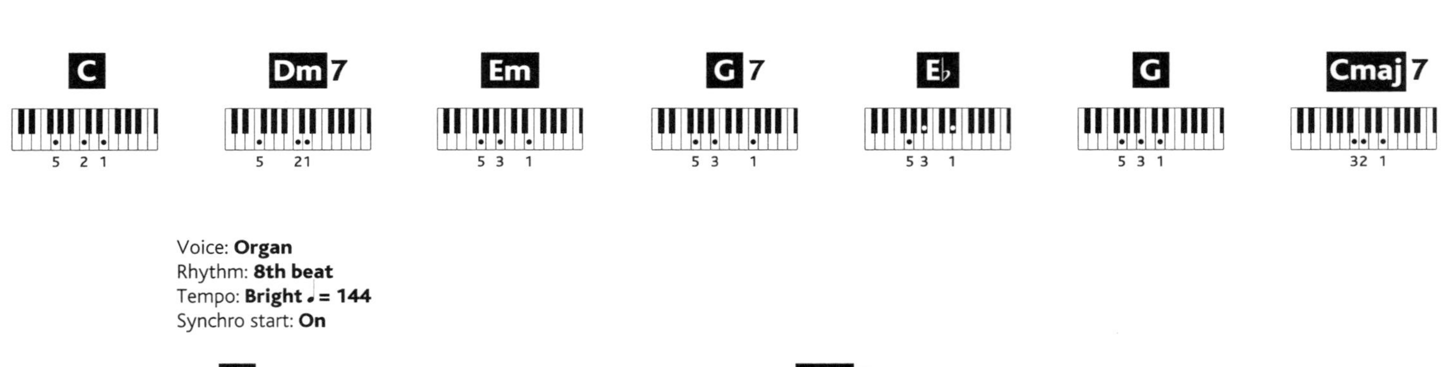
C
Dm7
Em
G7
E♭
G
Cmaj7
5 2 1
5 21
5 3 1
5 3 1
5 3 1
5 3 1
32 1
Voice: Organ
Rhythm: 8th beat
Tempo: Bright ♩ = 144
Synchro start: On

C
Dm7
1 G

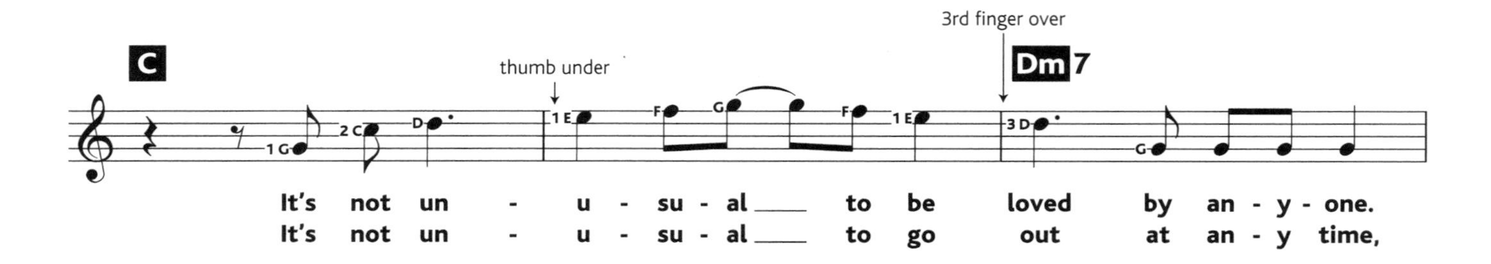
3rd finger over
thumb under
C
Dm7
1 G
2 C
D
1 E
F
G
G
F
1 E
3 D
G
It's not un - u - su - al ___ to be loved by an - y - one.
It's not un - u - su - al ___ to go out at an - y time,

C
thumb under
1 G
2 C
D
1 E
F
G
F
1 E
It's not un - u - su - al ___ to have
but when I see you out ___ and a -

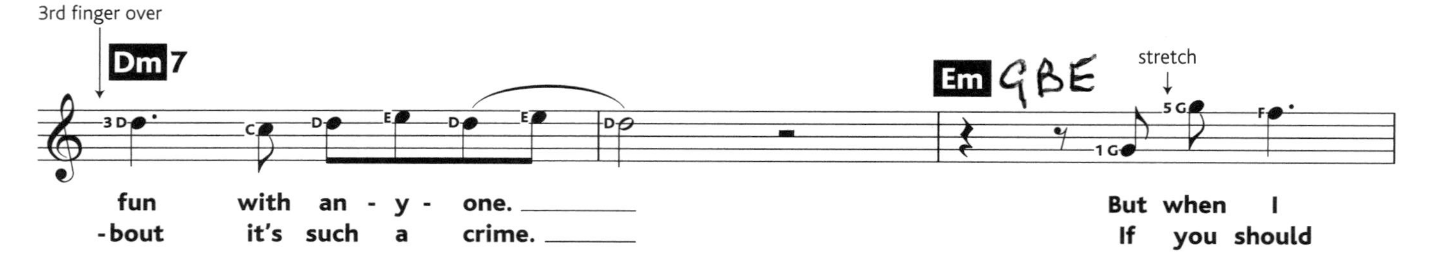
3rd finger over
Dm7
Em
stretch
3 D
C
D
E
D
E
D
1 G
5 G
F
fun with an - y - one. ___
-bout it's such a crime. ___
But when I
If you should

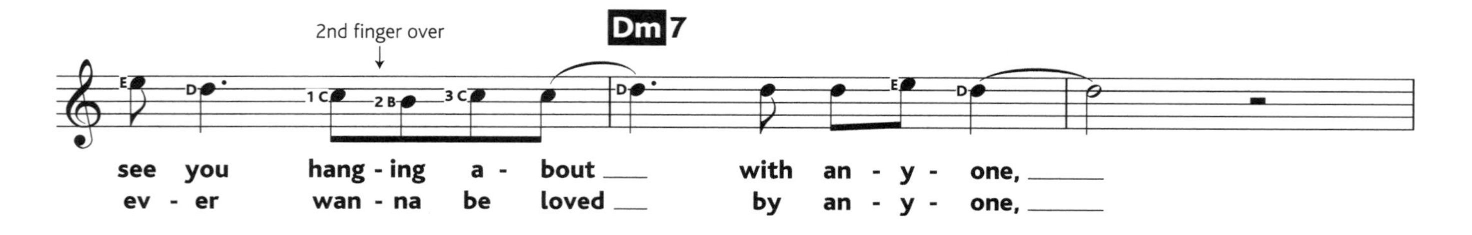
2nd finger over
Dm7
E
D
1 C
2 B
3 C
E
D
see you hang - ing a - bout ___ with an - y - one, ___
ev - er wan - na be loved ___ by an - y - one, ___

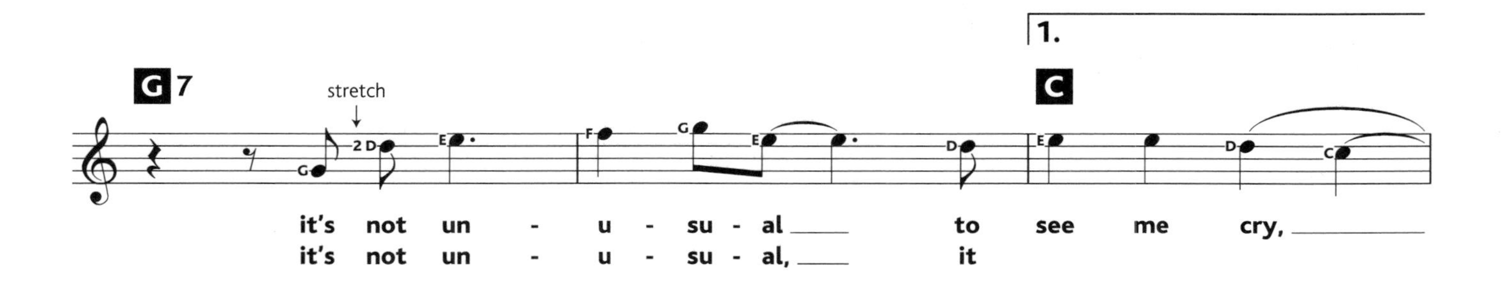
1.
G7
stretch
C
it's not un - u - su - al to see me cry,
it's not un - u - su - al, it

new hand position
Dm7
G7
I wan - na die.

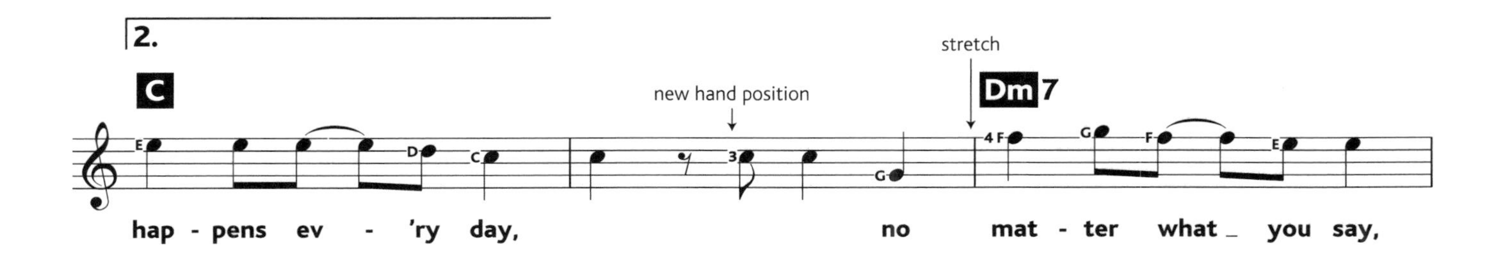
2.
C
new hand position
stretch
Dm7
hap - pens ev - 'ry day, no mat - ter what you say,

G7
you'll find it hap - pens all the

C
time. Love will nev - er do

Dm7
G7
thumb under
what you want it to. Why can't this cra - zy love be

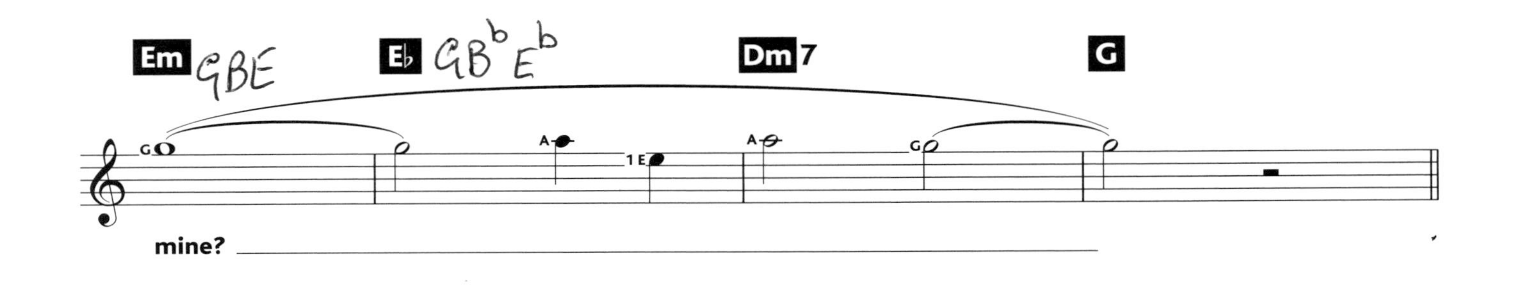
Em GBE
E♭ GB♭E♭
Dm7
G
G
A
1 E
A
G
mine?

Cmaj7 BCE
Dm7
2 B
E
B
A

Cmaj7 BCE
Dm7
2 B
E
B
A

Cmaj7 BCE
Dm7
2 B
E
B
A

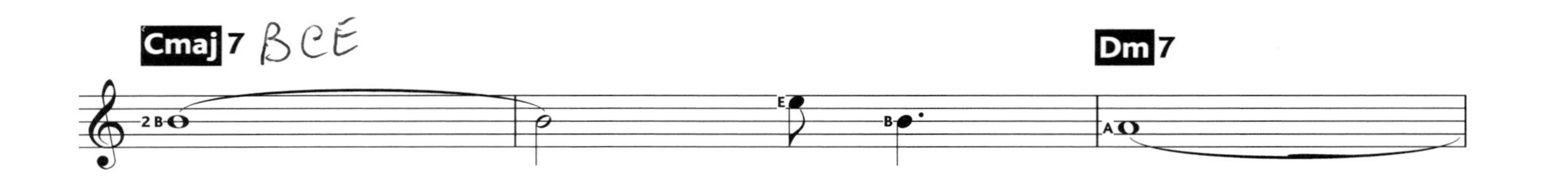
Cmaj7 BCE
Dm7
2 B
E
B
A

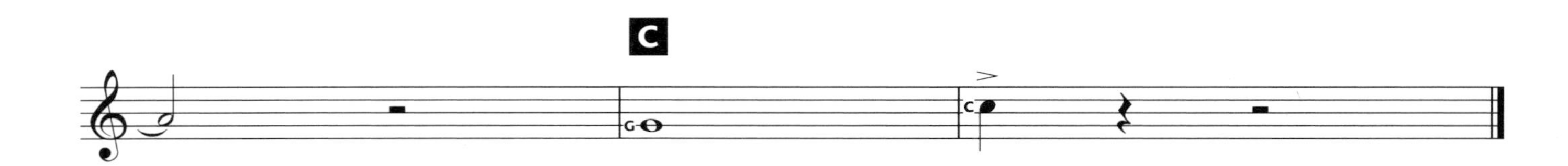
C
G
C

Runaway

Words & Music by Del Shannon & Max Crook

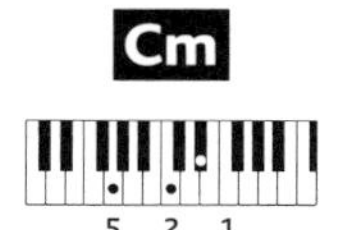
Cm
5 2 1
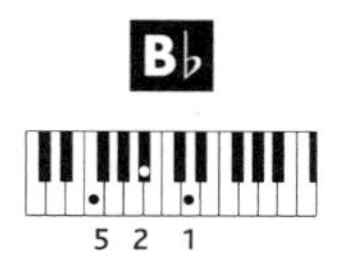
B♭
5 2 1
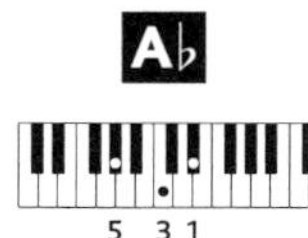
A♭
5 3 1
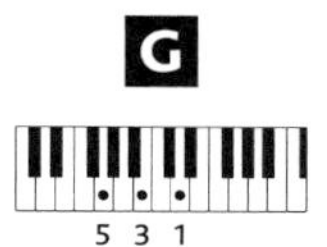
G
5 3 1
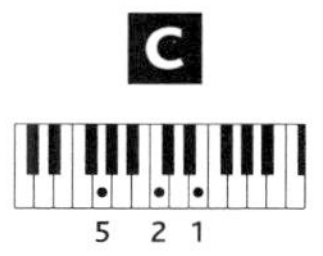
C
5 2 1
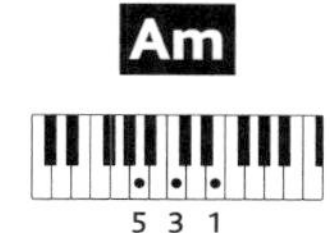
Am
5 3 1
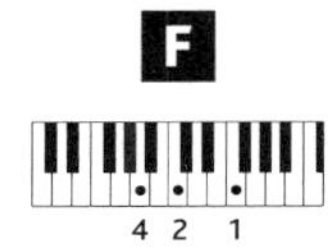
F
4 2 1

Voice: **Jazz organ**
Rhythm: **8th beat**
Tempo: **Not too fast ♩ = 130**
Synchro start: **On**

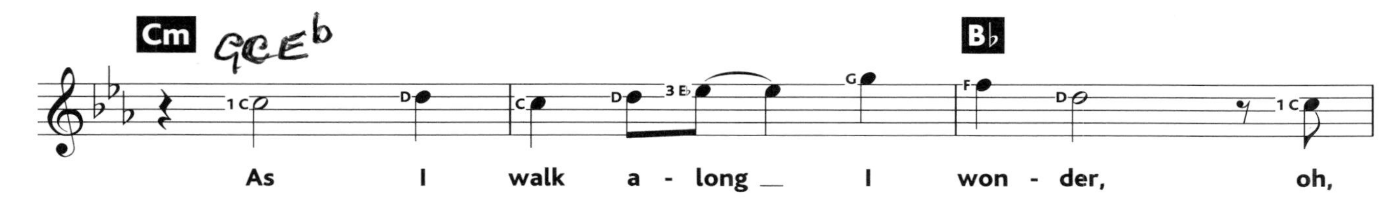
Cm
GCE♭
B♭
As I walk a - long I won - der, oh,

2nd finger over
A♭
A♭CE♭
2nd finger over
what went wrong with our love, a love that was so

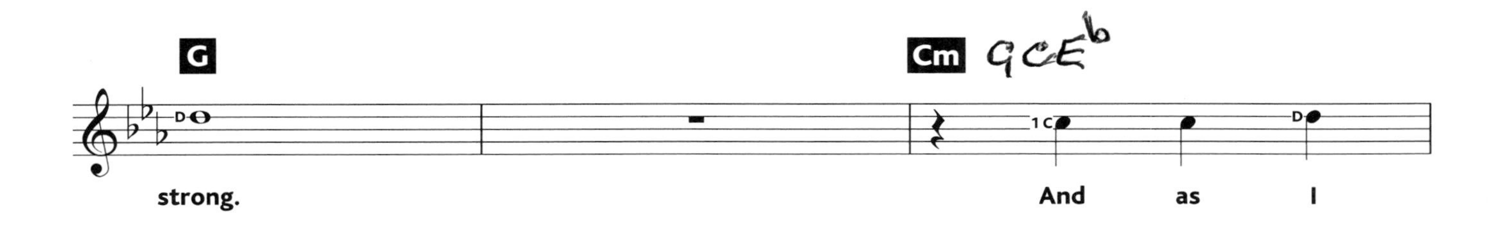
G
Cm
GCE♭
strong. And as I

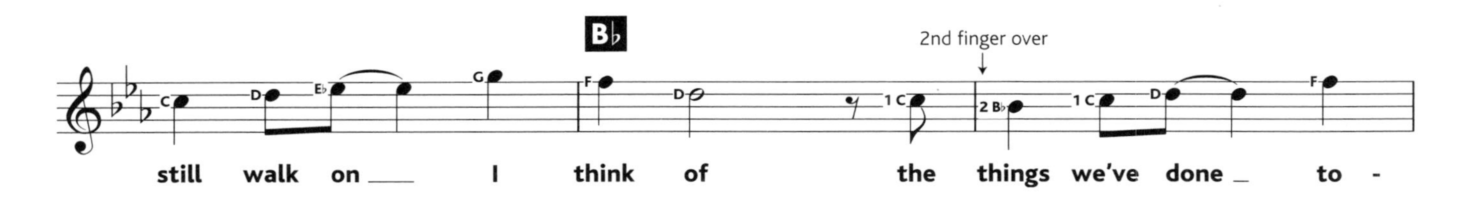
B♭
2nd finger over
still walk on I think of the things we've done to -

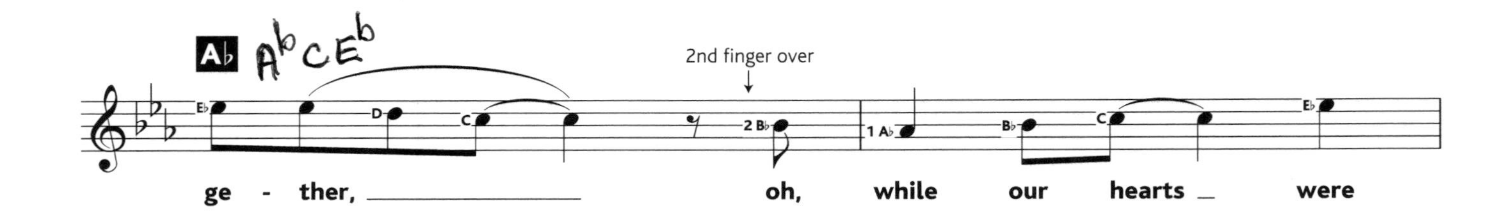
A♭
2nd finger over
ge - ther, oh, while our hearts were

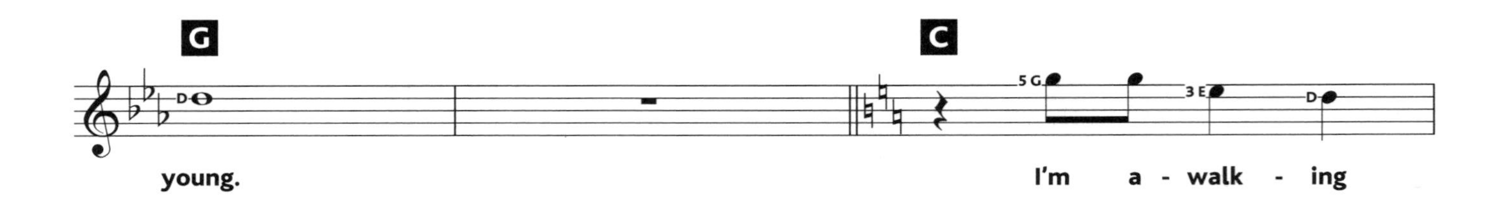
G
C
young. I'm a - walk - ing

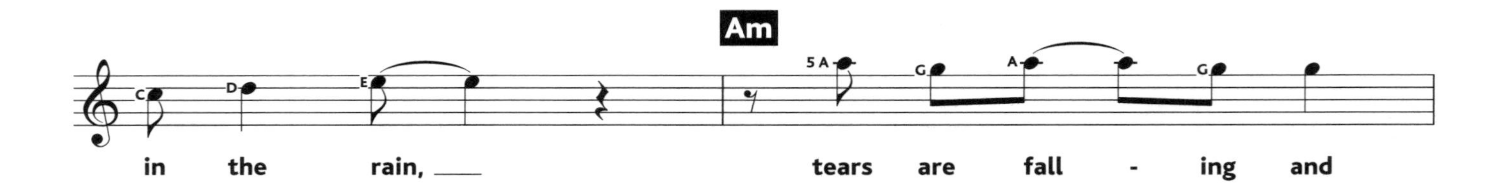
Am
in the rain, tears are fall - ing and

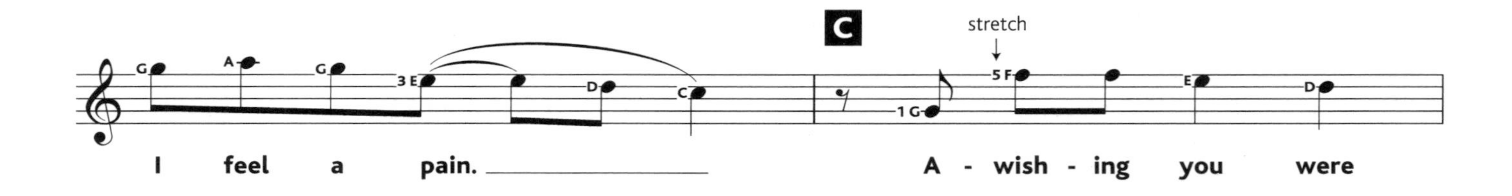
C
stretch
I feel a pain. A - wish - ing you were

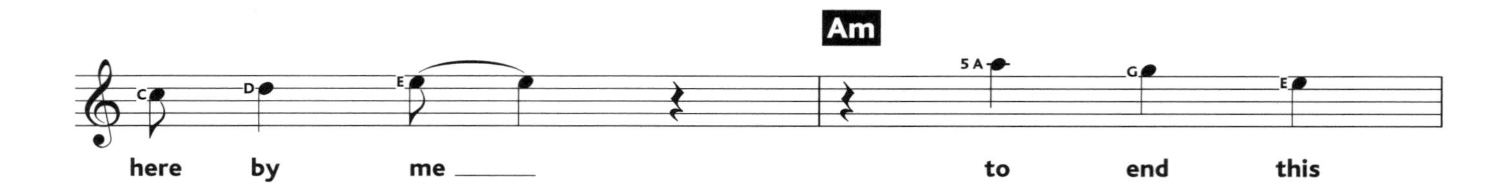
Am
here by me to end this

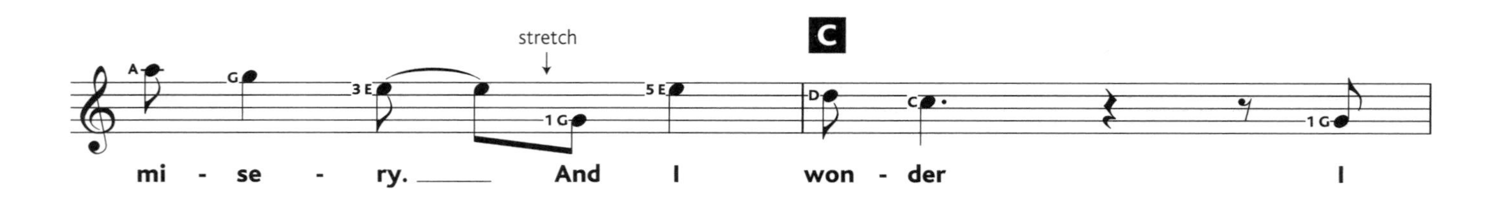
stretch
C
mi - se - ry. And I won - der I

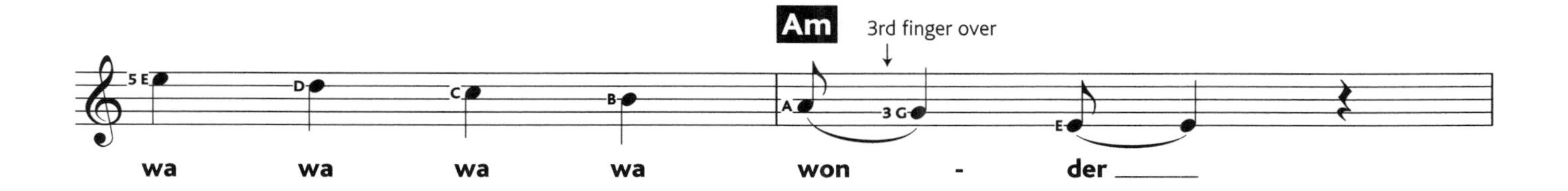
Am
3rd finger over
5 E
D
C
B
A
3 G
E
wa wa wa wa won - der

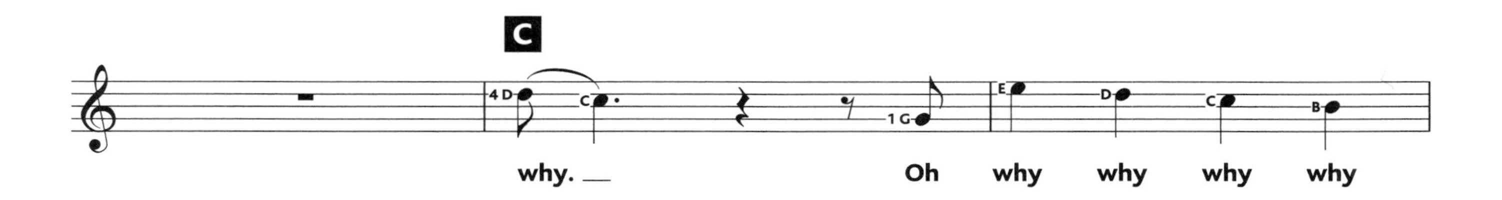
C
4 D
C
1 G
E
D
C
B
why.
Oh why why why why

Am
stretch
A
4 G
A
G
E
5 A
G
3 E
why she ran a - way. And I

F
new hand position
G
D
C
1 A
C
4 E
5 G
3 D
E
won - der where she will stay,

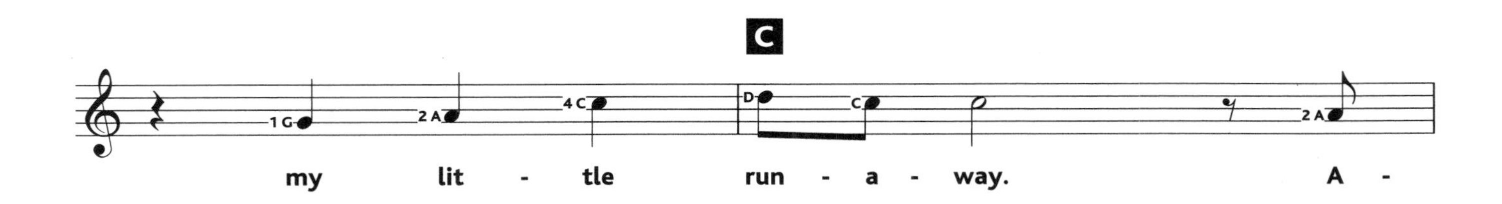
C
1 G
2 A
4 C
D
C
2 A
my lit - tle run - a - way. A -

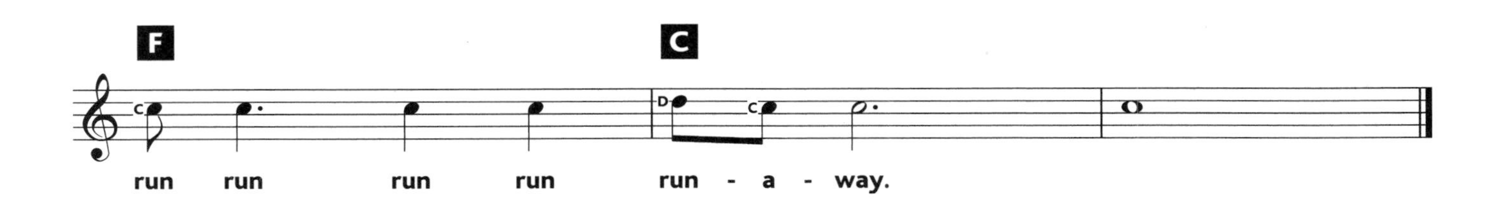
F
C
C
D
C
run run run run run - a - way.

It's Now Or Never

Words & Music by Wally Gold, Aaron Schroeder & Eduardo Di Capua

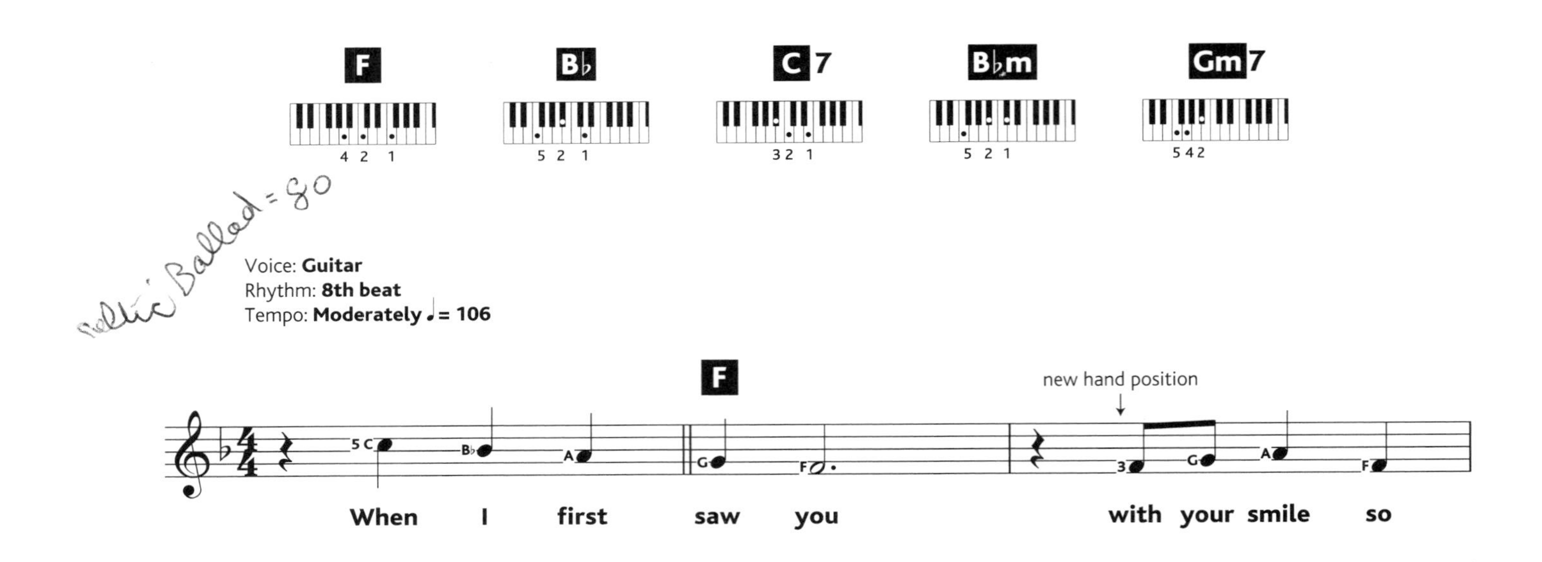
F
B♭
C7
B♭m
Gm7
4 2 1
5 2 1
3 2 1
5 2 1
5 4 2
Ballad = 80
Voice: Guitar
Rhythm: 8th beat
Tempo: Moderately ♩= 106
new hand position
When I first saw you with your smile so

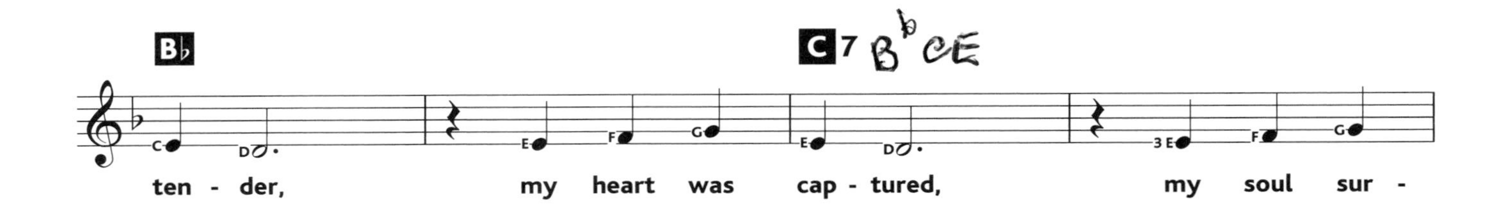
B♭
C7
B♭ C E
ten - der, my heart was cap - tured, my soul sur -

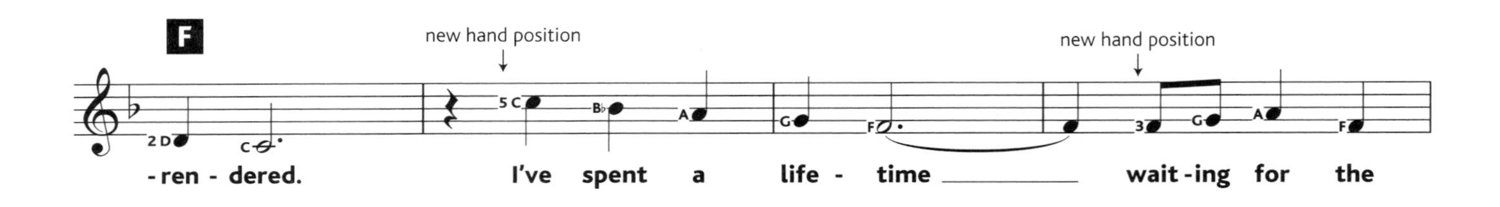
F
new hand position
new hand position
- ren - dered. I've spent a life - time wait - ing for the

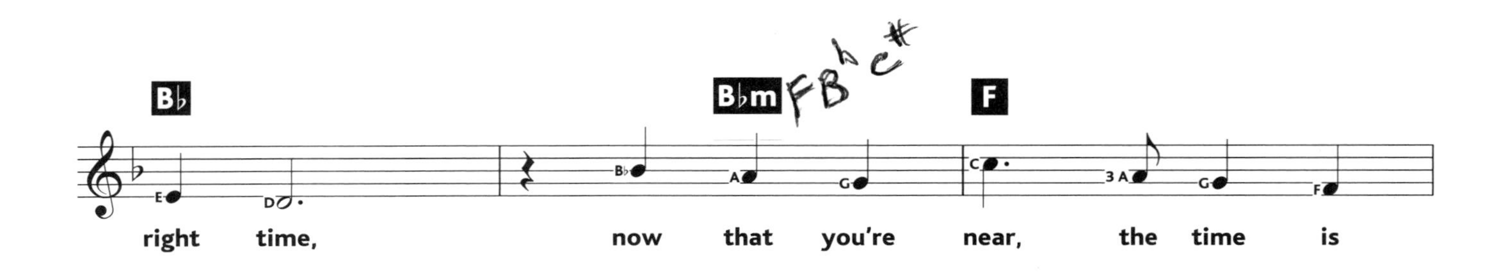
B♭
B♭m
F
right time, now that you're near, the time is

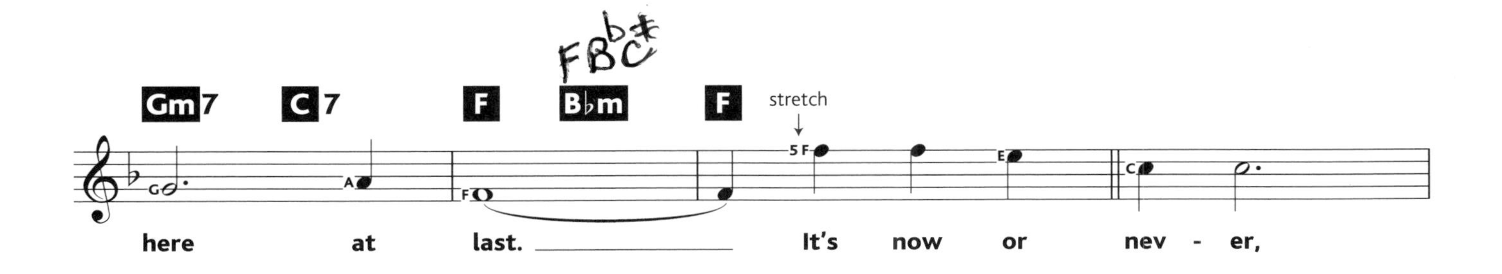
Gm7 C7 F B♭m F
FB♭C♯
stretch
here at last. It's now or nev - er,

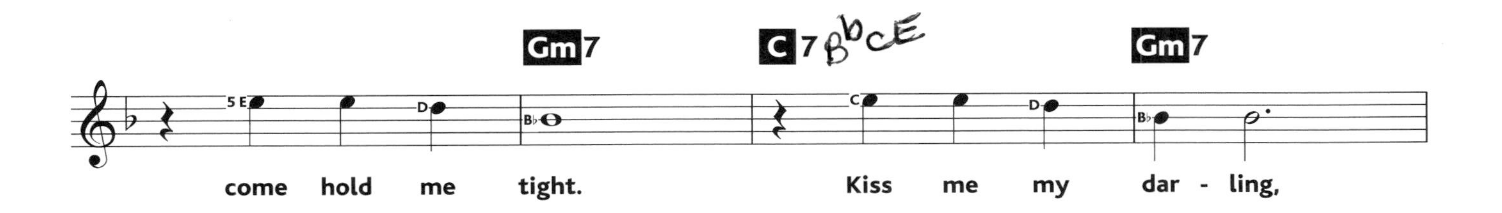
Gm7 C7 Gm7
B♭CE
come hold me tight. Kiss me my dar - ling,

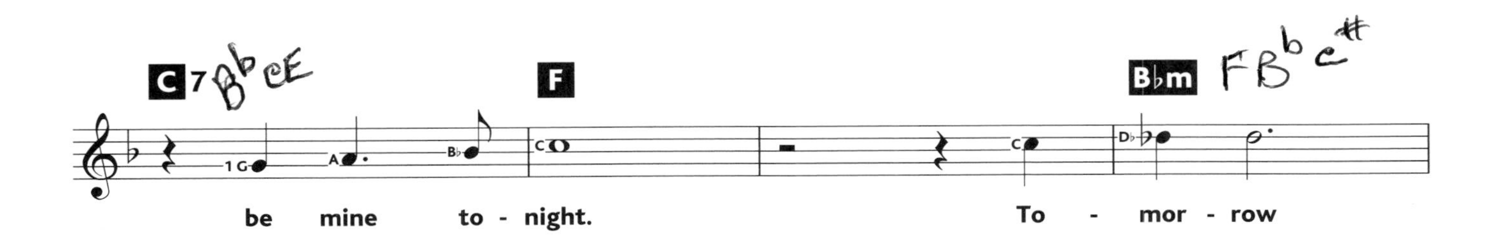
C7 F B♭m
B♭CE
FB♭C♯
be mine to - night. To - mor - row

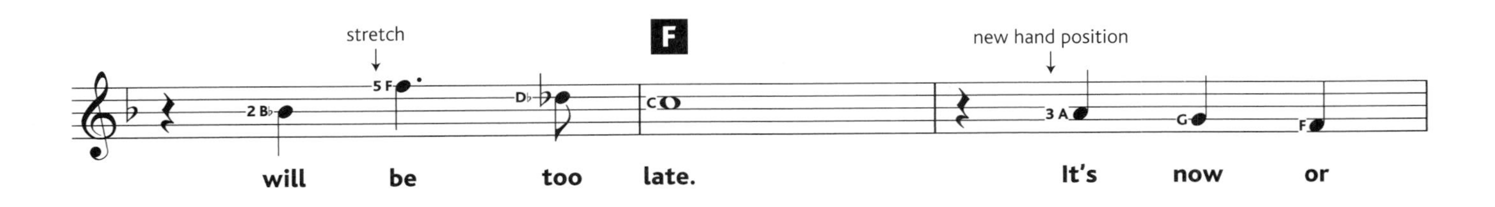
F
stretch
new hand position
will be too late. It's now or

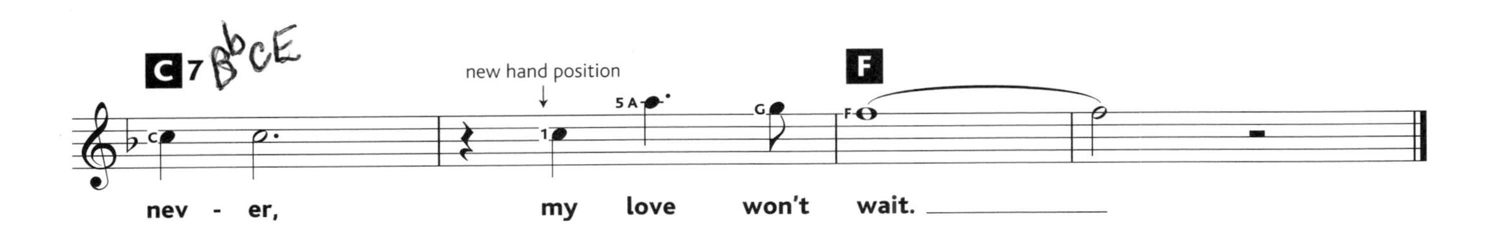
C7 F
B♭CE
new hand position
nev - er, my love won't wait.

Magic Moments

Words by Hal David
Music by Burt Bacharach

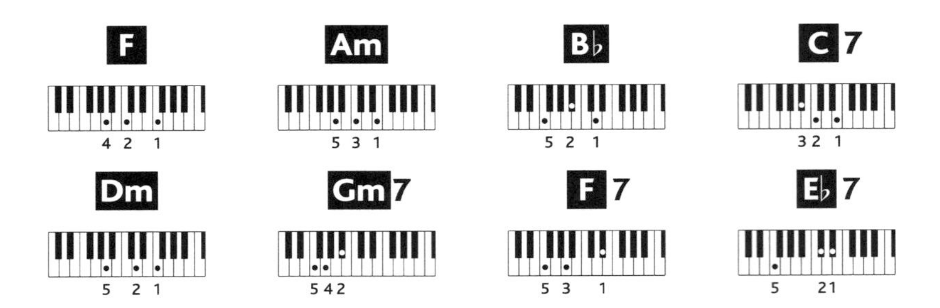
F
4 2 1
Am
5 3 1
B♭
5 2 1
C7
3 2 1
Dm
5 2 1
Gm7
5 4 2
F7
5 3 1
E♭7
5 21

Voice: **Clarinet**
Rhythm: **Swing**
Tempo: **Moderately ♩. = 110**
Synchro start: **On**

new hand position

F Am B♭ C7 F

12/8 1 F C 1 E C 3 D E F

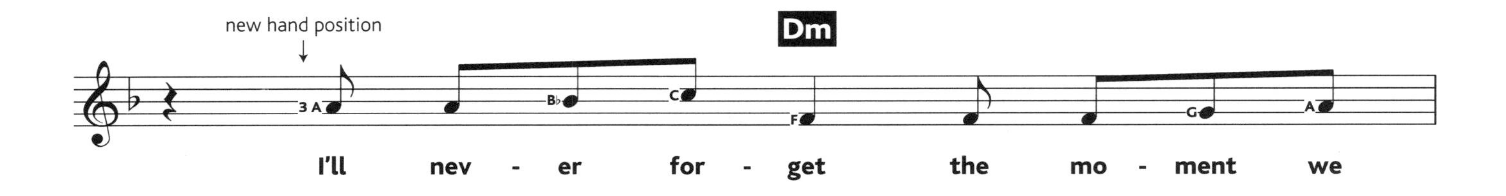
new hand position
Dm
3 A A B♭ C F F F G A
I'll nev - er for - get the mo - ment we

Gm7
C7
1 D D D E F 5 A G
kissed, the night of the hay ride,

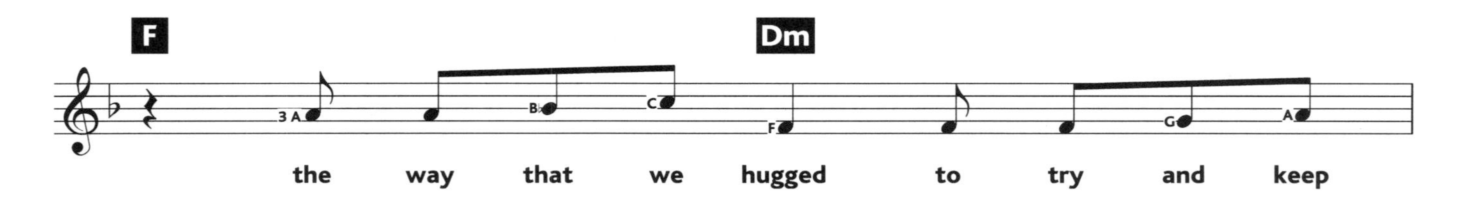
F
Dm
3 A A B♭ C F F F G A
the way that we hugged to try and keep

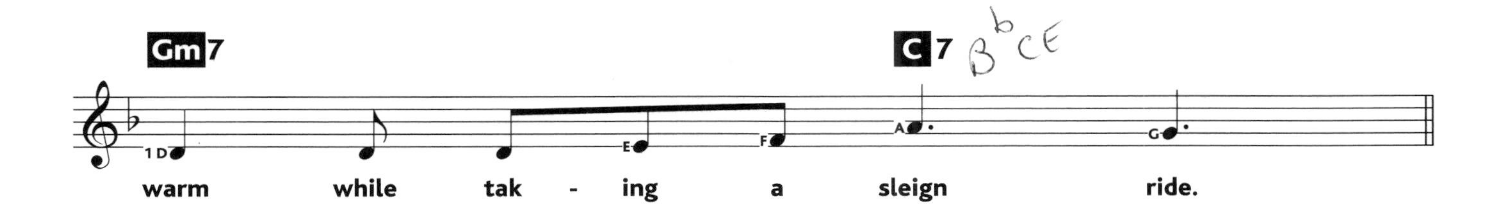
Gm7
C7
B♭ C E
1 D
E
F
A
G
warm while tak - ing a sleign ride.

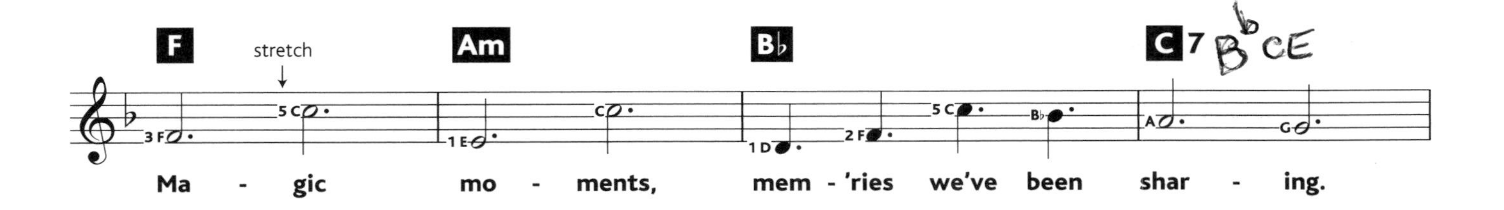
F
Am
B♭
C7
B♭ C E
stretch
3 F
5 C
1 E
C
1 D
2 F
5 C
B♭
A
G
Ma - gic mo - ments, mem - 'ries we've been shar - ing.

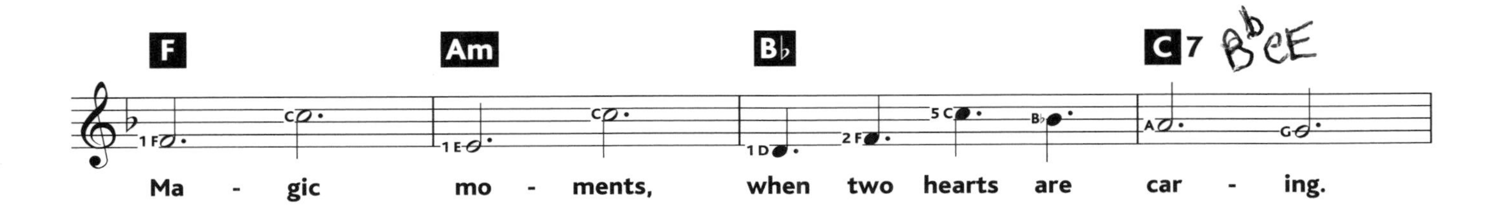
F
Am
B♭
C7
B♭ C E
1 F
C
1 E
C
1 D
2 F
5 C
B♭
A
G
Ma - gic mo - ments, when two hearts are car - ing.

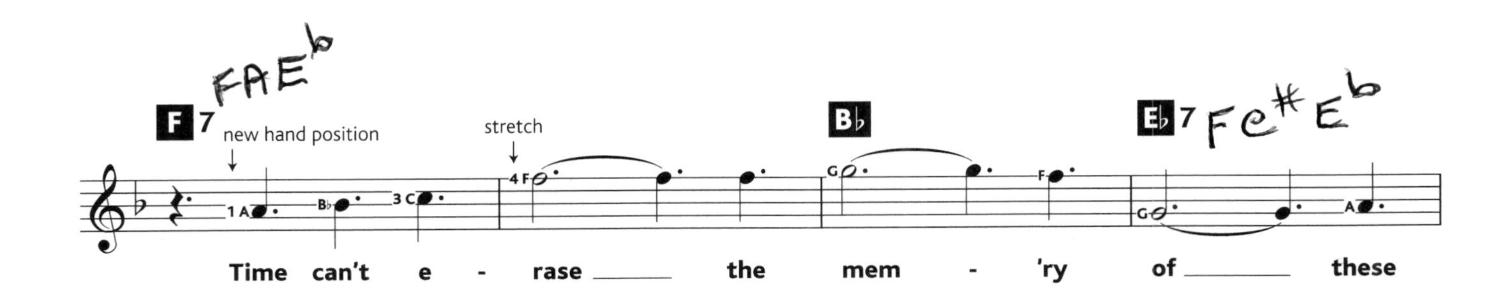
F7
F A E♭
B♭
E♭7
F C# E♭
new hand position
stretch
1 A
B♭
3 C
4 F
G
F
G
A
Time can't e - rase the mem - 'ry of these

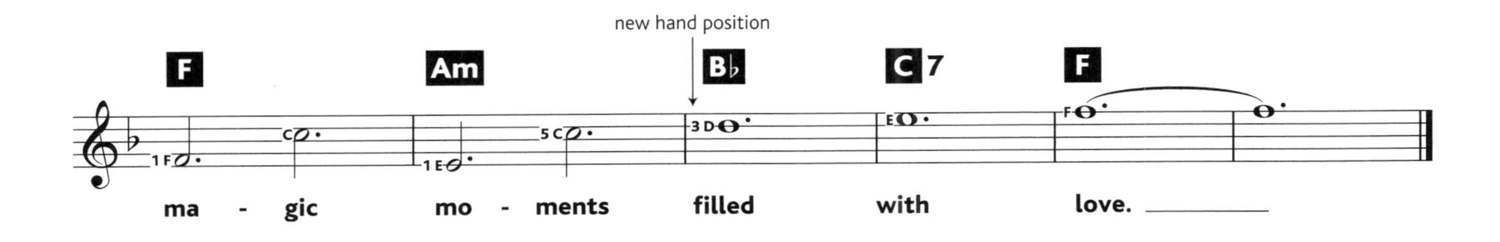
F
Am
B♭
C7
F
new hand position
1 F
C
1 E
5 C
3 D
E
F
ma - gic mo - ments filled with love.

Mona Lisa

Words & Music by Jay Livingston & Ray Evans

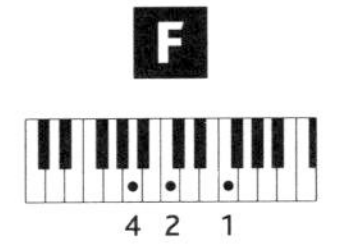
F
4 2 1
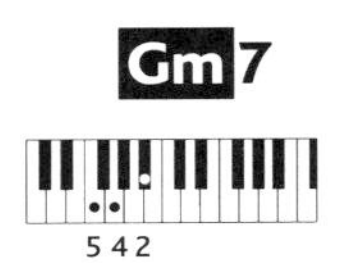
Gm7
5 4 2
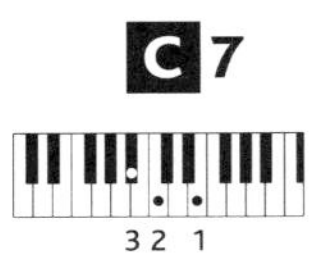
C7
3 2 1
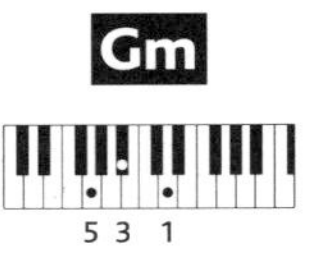
Gm
5 3 1
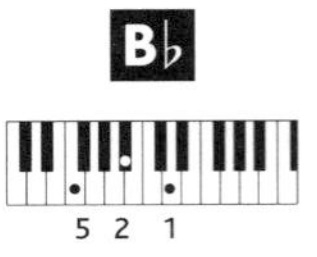
B♭
5 2 1
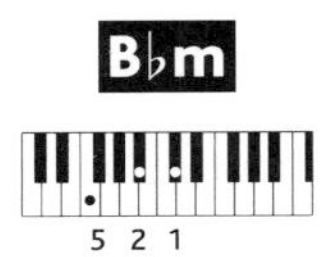
B♭m
5 2 1
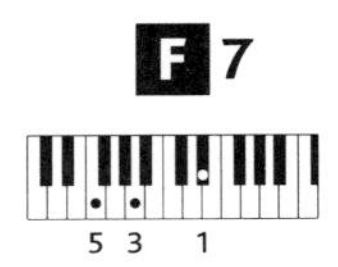
F7
5 3 1

Voice: **Piano**
Rhythm: **Bossa nova**
Tempo: **Moderately** ♩ **= 104**

F
2nd finger over
stretch
Mo - na Li - sa, Mo - na Li - sa men have named you. You're so

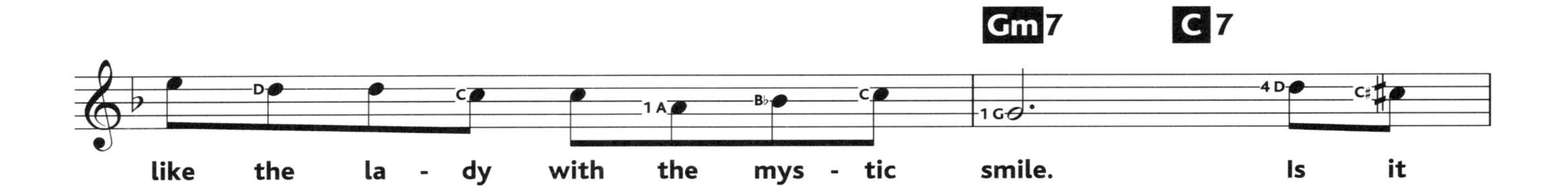
Gm7
C7
like the la - dy with the mys - tic smile. Is it

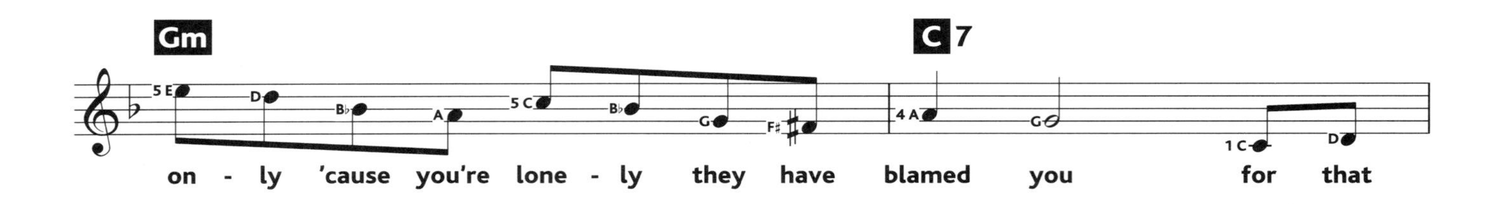
Gm
C7
on - ly 'cause you're lone - ly they have blamed you for that

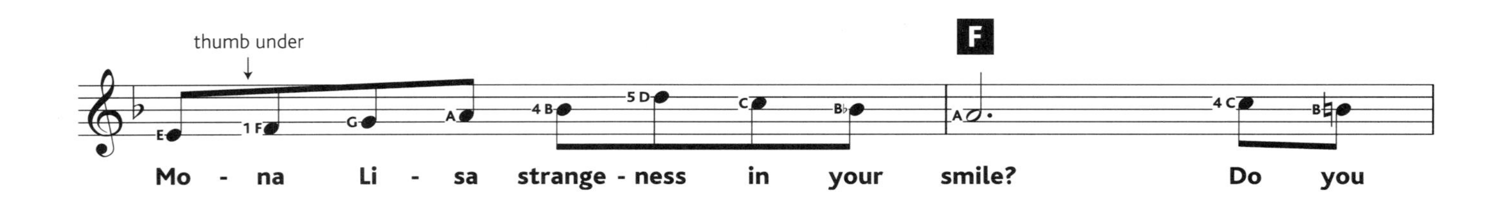
thumb under
F
Mo - na Li - sa strange - ness in your smile? Do you

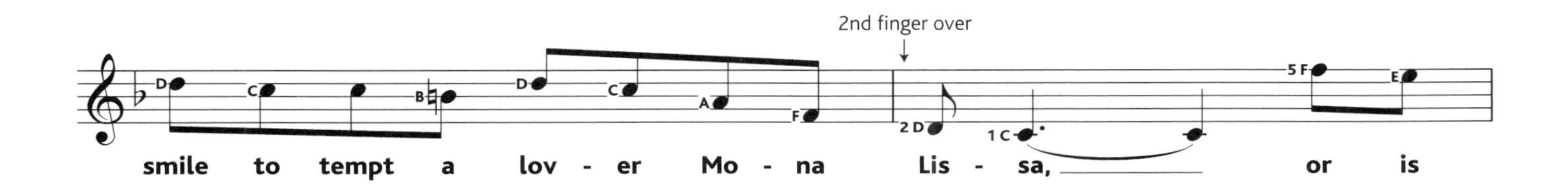
2nd finger over
smile to tempt a lov - er Mo - na Lis - sa, or is

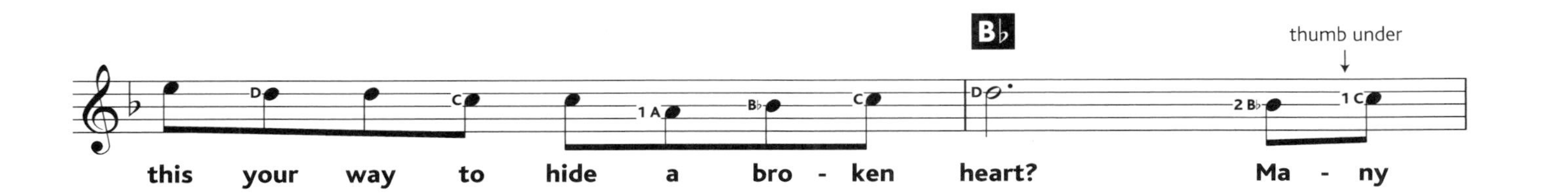
B♭
thumb under
this your way to hide a bro - ken heart? Ma - ny

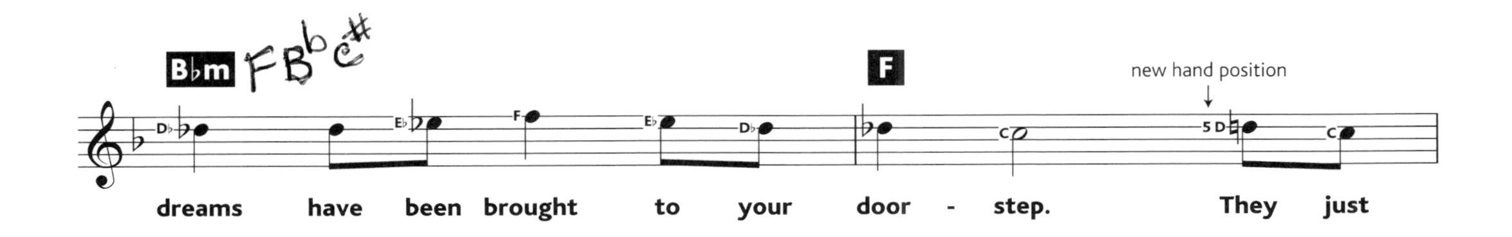
B♭m
F
new hand position
dreams have been brought to your door - step. They just

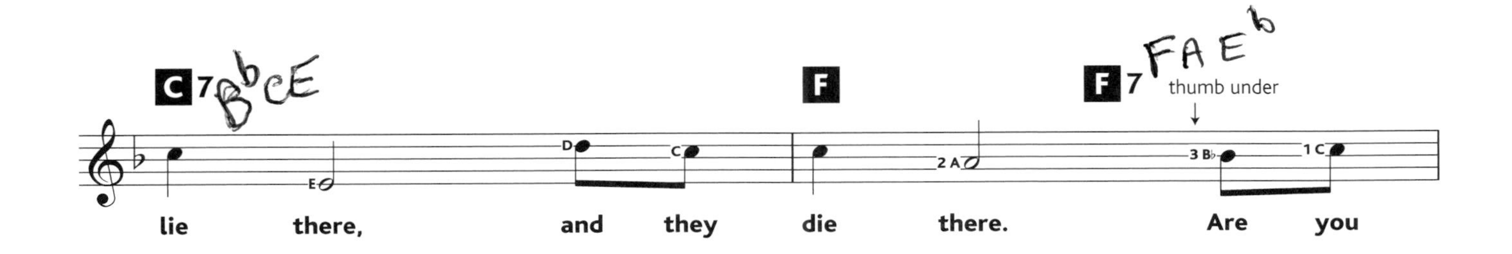
C7
F
F7
thumb under
lie there, and they die there. Are you

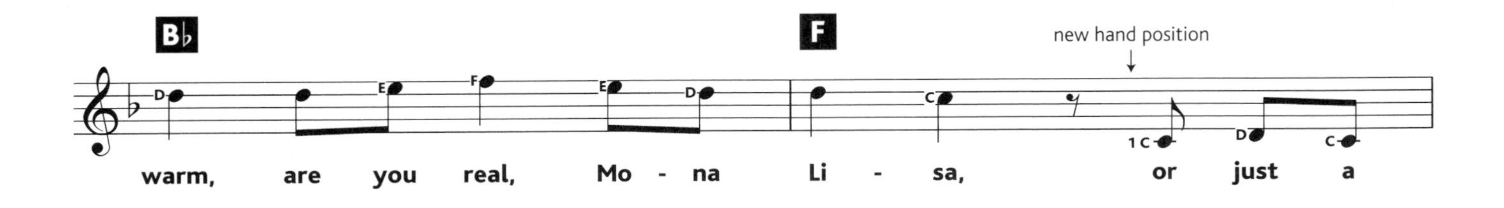
B♭
F
new hand position
warm, are you real, Mo - na Li - sa, or just a

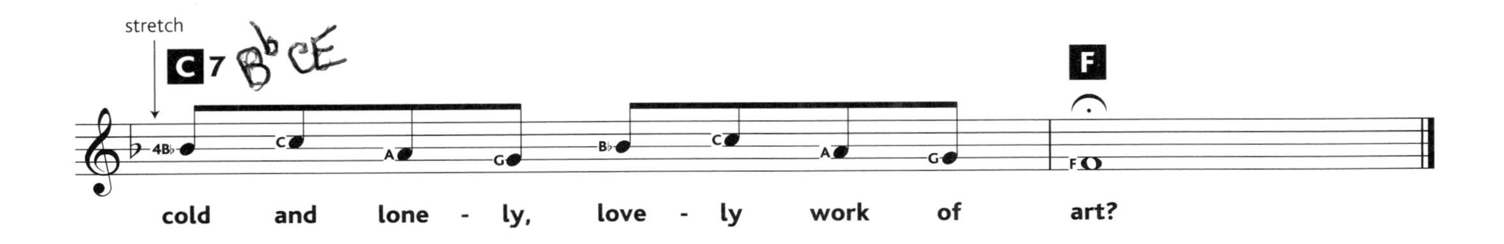
stretch
C7
F
cold and lone - ly, love - ly work of art?

Ring Of Fire

Words & Music by Merle Kilgore & June Carter

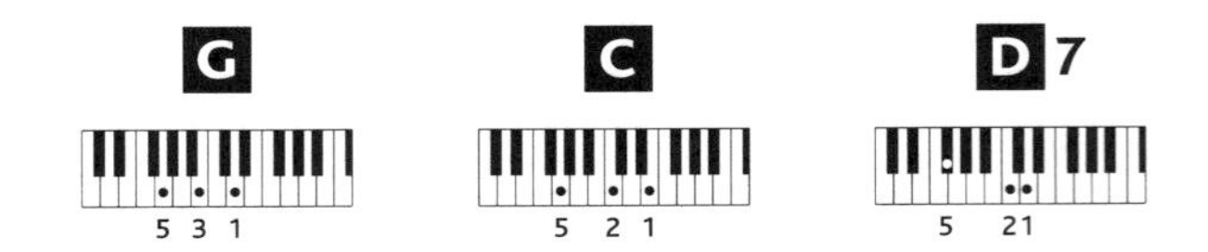
G
C
D7
5 3 1
5 2 1
5 21

Voice: **Saxophone**
Rhythm: **8th beat**
Tempo: **Brightly ♩ = 172**
Synchro start: **On**

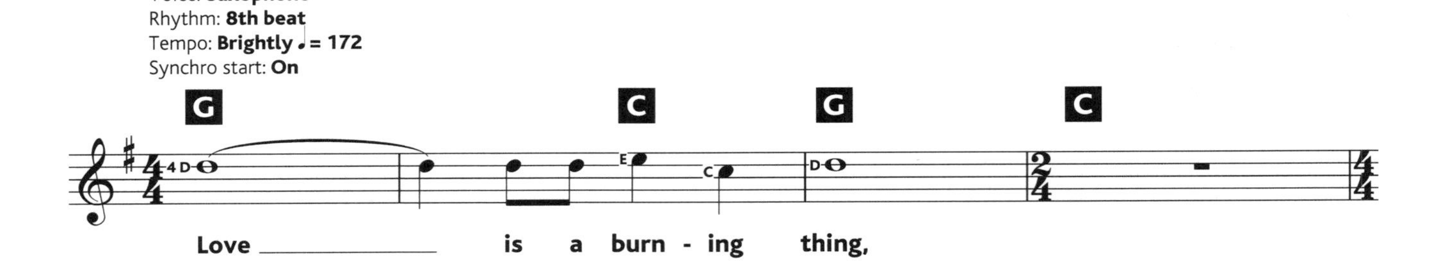
G
C
G
C
4 D
E
C
D
Love
is a burn - ing thing,

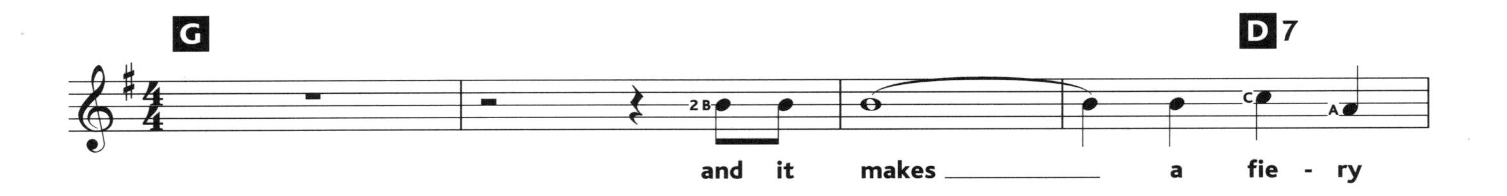
G
D7
2 B
C
A
and it makes
a fie - ry

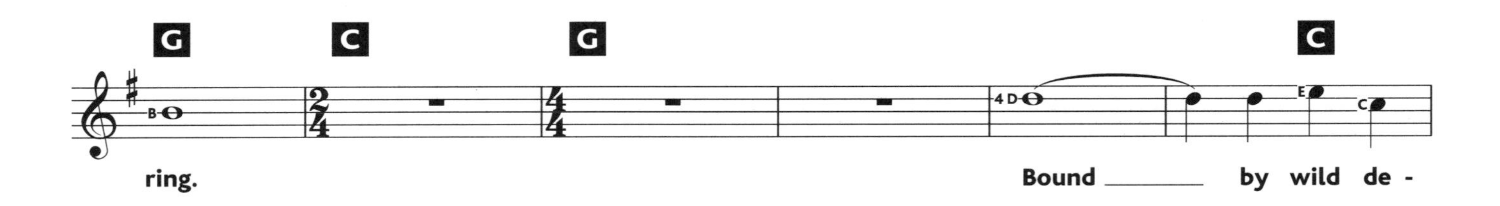
G
C
G
C
B
4 D
E
C
ring.
Bound
by wild de -

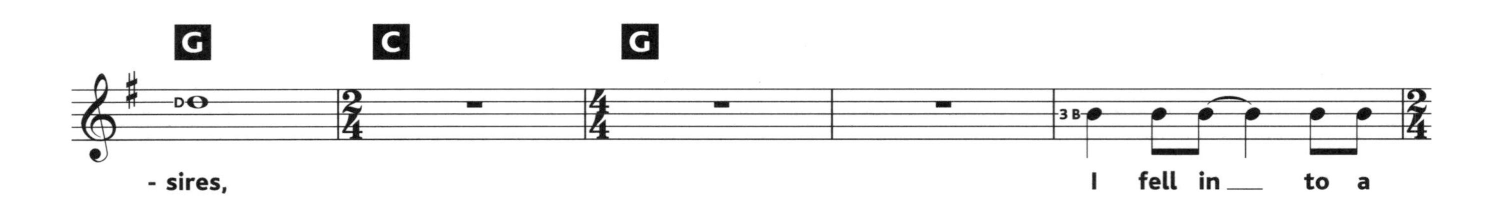
G
C
G
D
3 B
- sires,
I fell in
to a

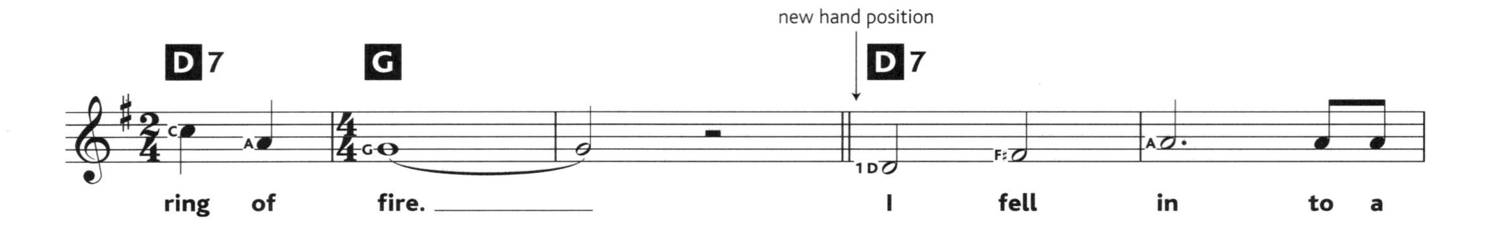
new hand position
D7
G
D7
C
A
G
1 D
F♯
A
ring of fire.
I fell in to a

C
G
D7
burn - ing ring of fire. I went down, down,

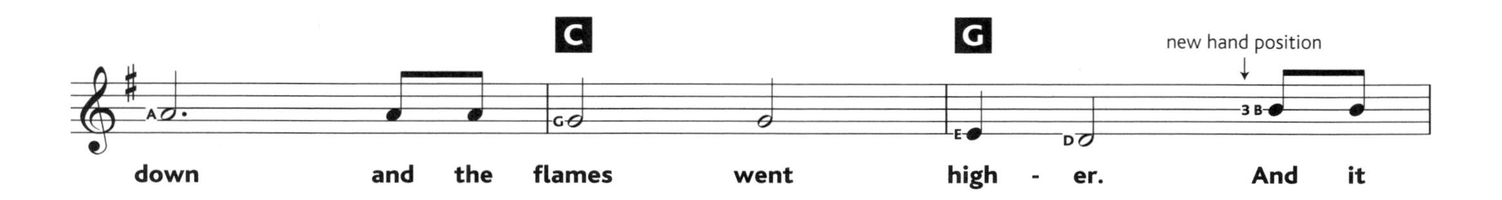
C
G
new hand position
down and the flames went high - er. And it

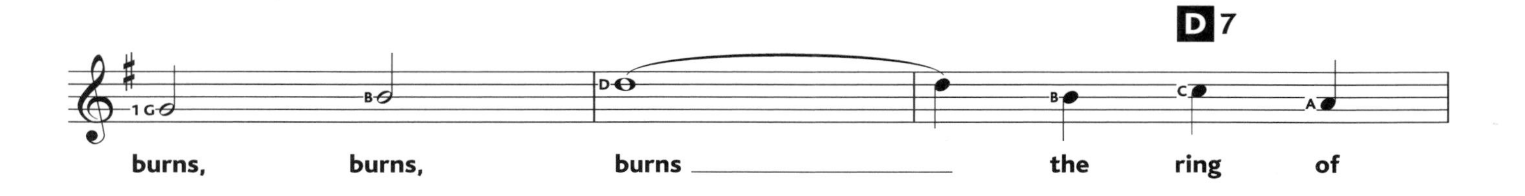
D7
burns, burns, burns the ring of

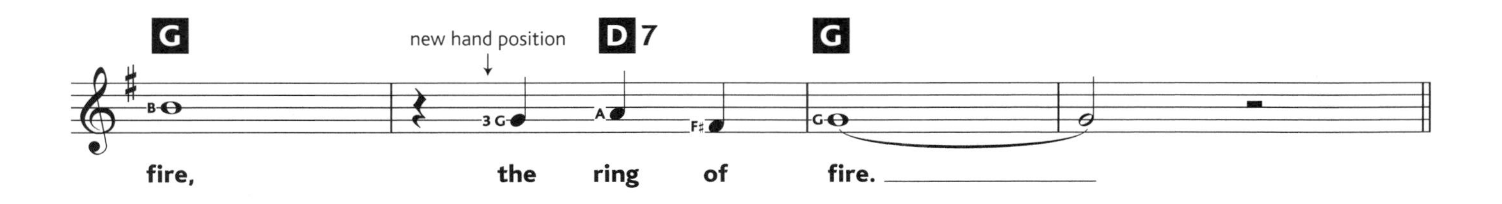
G
new hand position
D7
G
fire, the ring of fire.

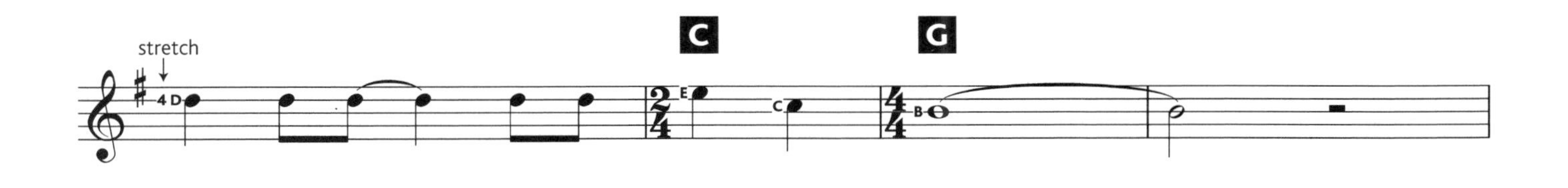
stretch
C
G

new hand position
C
G

Telstar

Music by Joe Meek

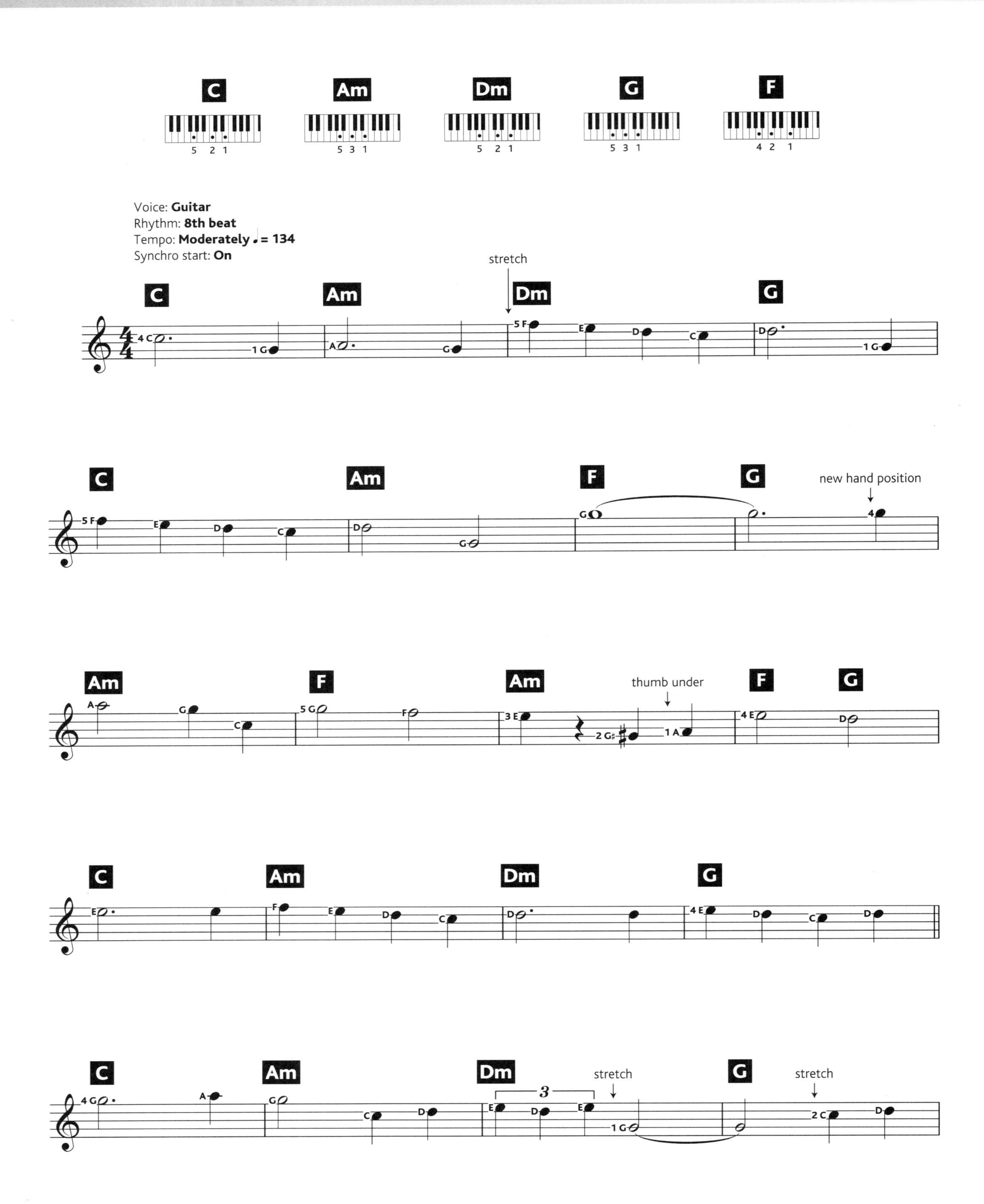

C
Am
Dm
G
F
5 2 1
5 3 1
5 2 1
5 3 1
4 2 1
Voice: Guitar
Rhythm: 8th beat
Tempo: Moderately ♩ = 134
Synchro start: On
stretch
new hand position
thumb under
stretch
stretch
3

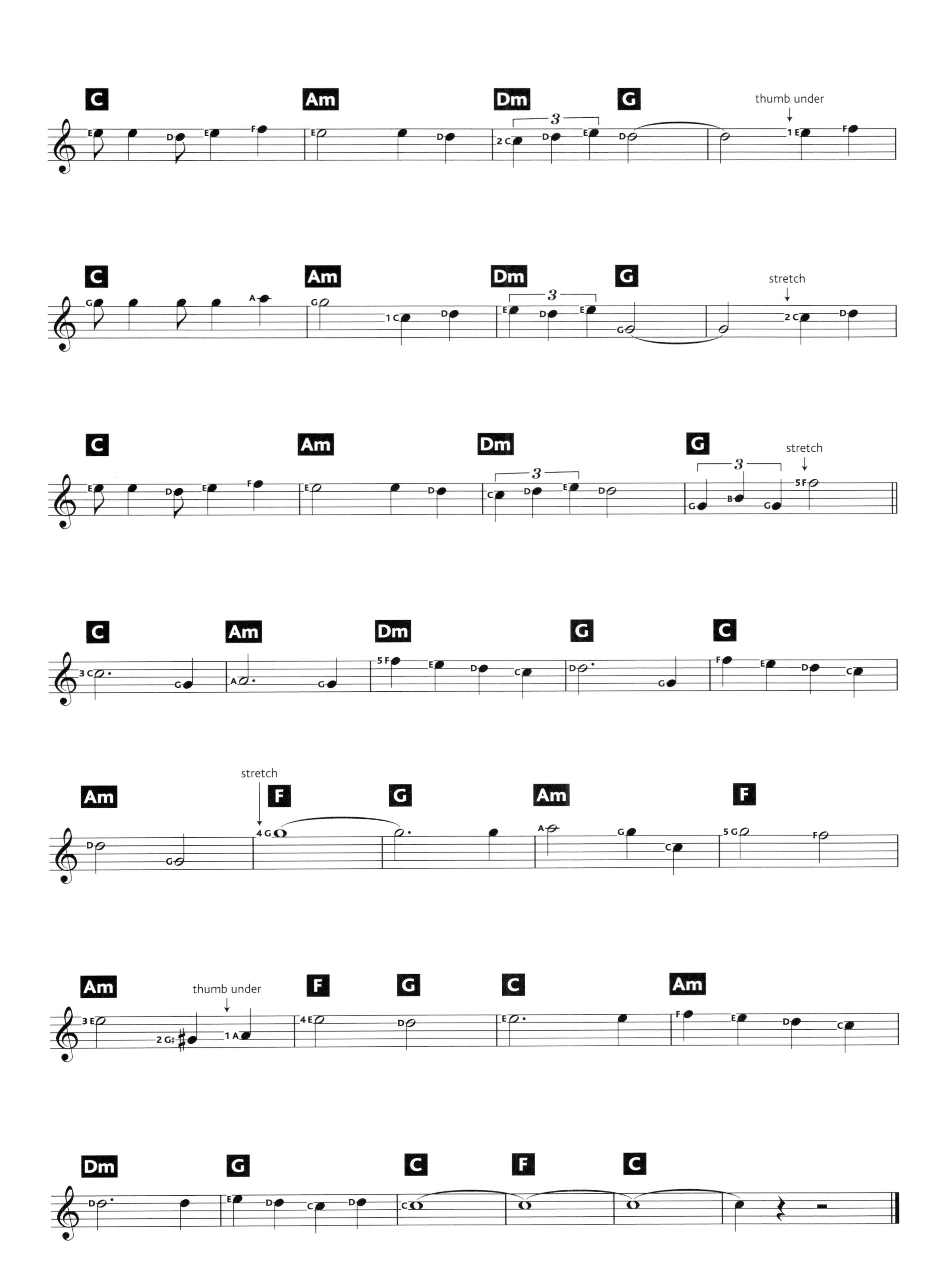
C Am Dm G
thumb under
C Am Dm G
stretch
C Am Dm G
stretch
C Am Dm G C
Am F G Am F
stretch
Am F G C Am
thumb under
Dm G C F C

That's Amoré

Words & Music by Harry Warren & Jack Brooks

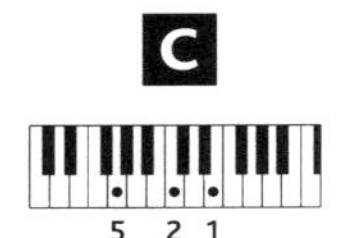
C
5 2 1

G7
5 3 1
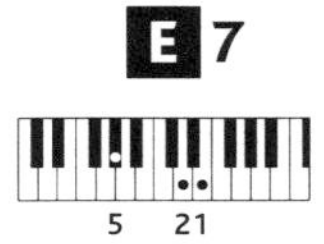
E7
5 21
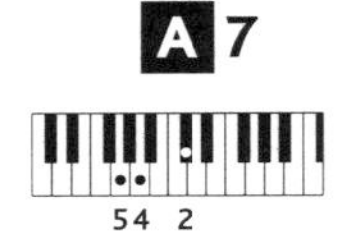
A7
54 2
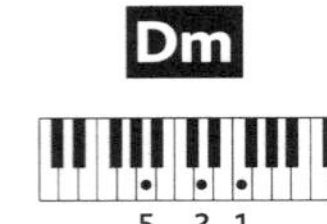
Dm
5 2 1
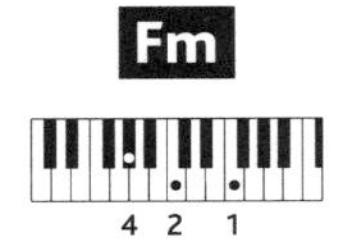
Fm
4 2 1

Voice: **Mandolin**
Rhythm: **Waltz**
Tempo: **Not too fast ♩ = 160**

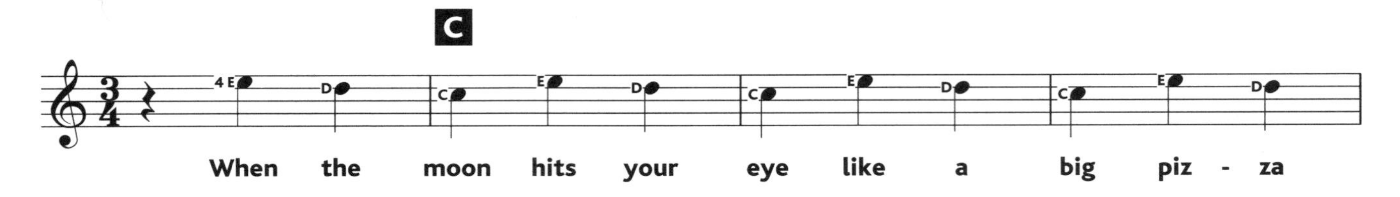
C
When the moon hits your eye like a big piz - za

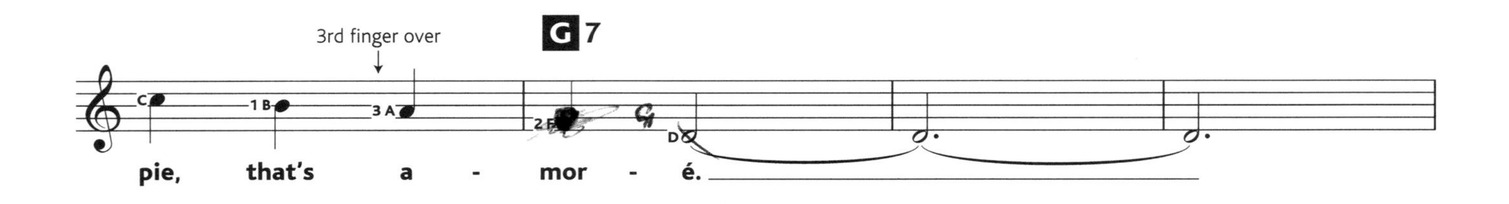
3rd finger over
G7
pie, that's a - mor - é.

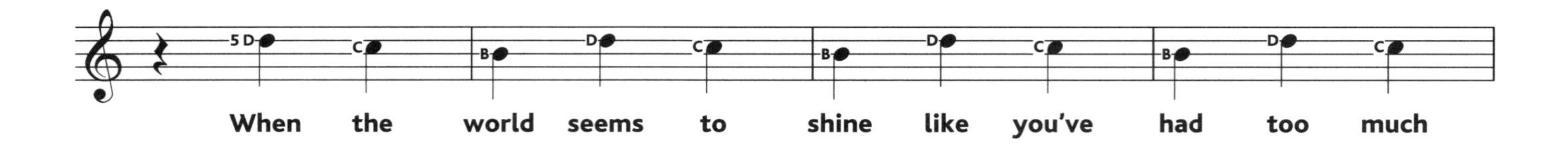
When the world seems to shine like you've had too much

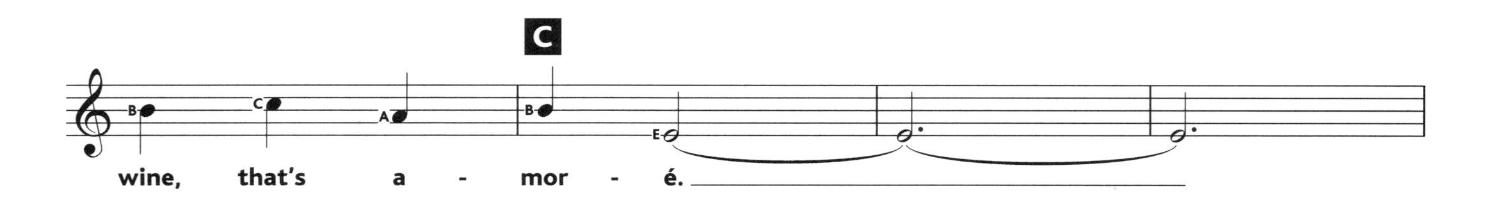
C
wine, that's a - mor - é.

1 E G C E G E G C E G E G C E G
Bells will ring, ting - a - ling - a - ling, ting - a - ling - a - ling, and you'll

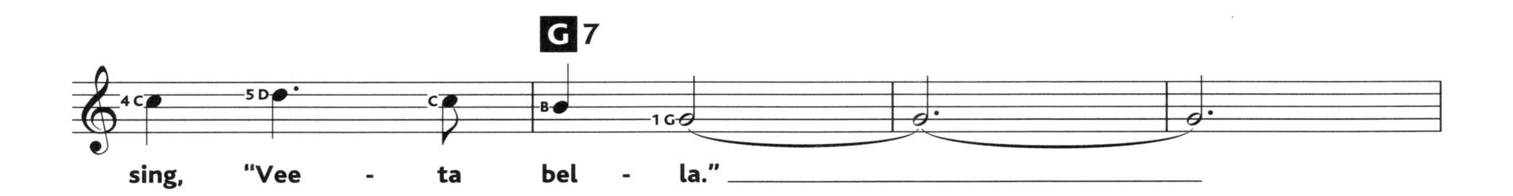
G7
4 C 5 D C B 1 G
sing, "Vee - ta bel - la."

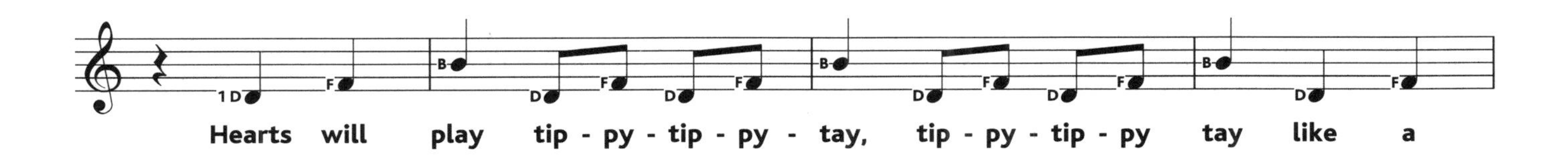
1 D F B D F D F B D F D F B D F
Hearts will play tip - py - tip - py - tay, tip - py - tip - py tay like a

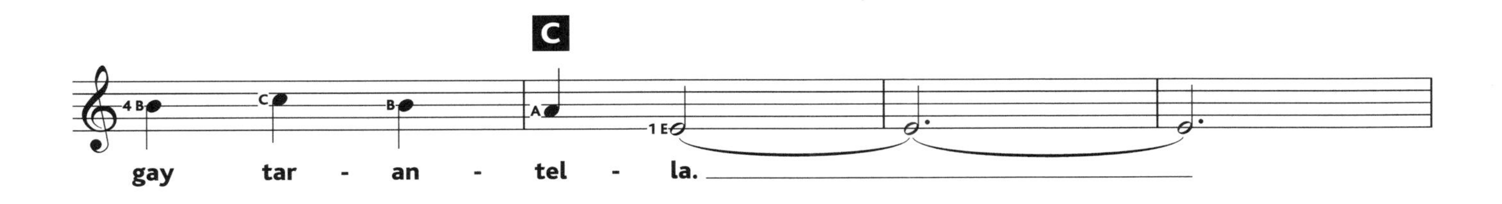
C
4 B C B A 1 E
gay tar - an - tel - la.

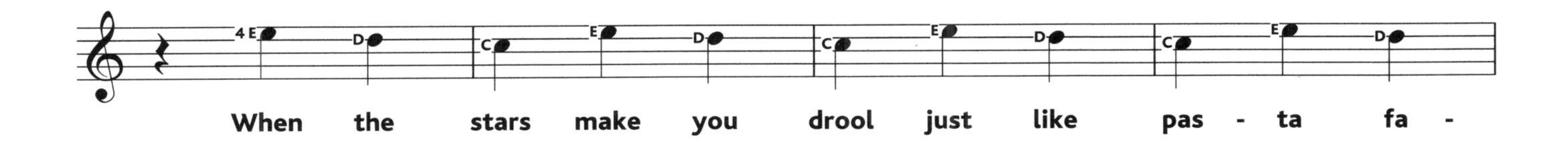
4 E D C E D C E D C E D
When the stars make you drool just like pas - ta fa -

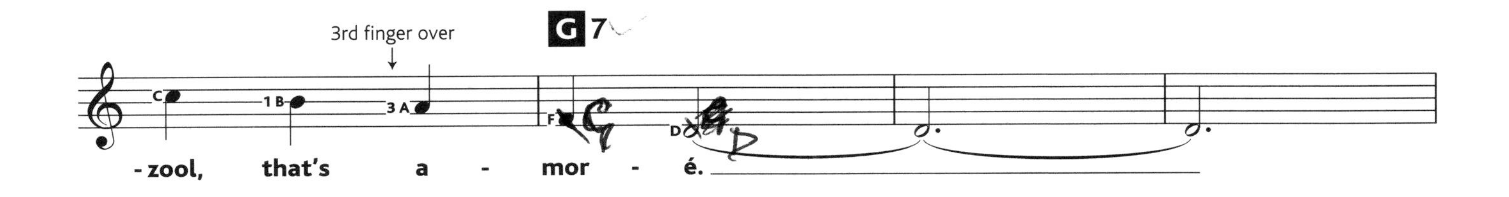
3rd finger over
G7
C 1 B 3 A F D
- zool, that's a - mor - é.

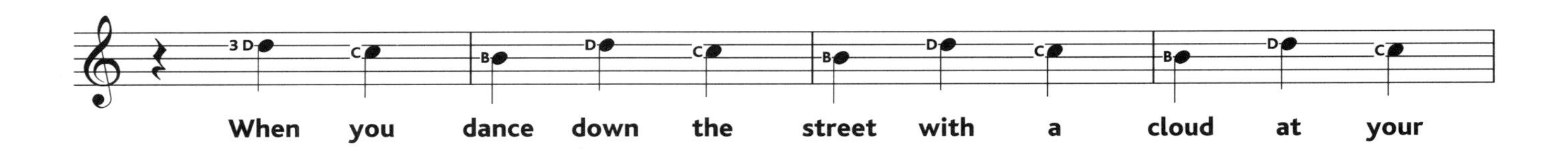
3 D C B D C B D C B D C
When you dance down the street with a cloud at your

E7 A7
1 B 3 A 2 F E
feet, you're in love.

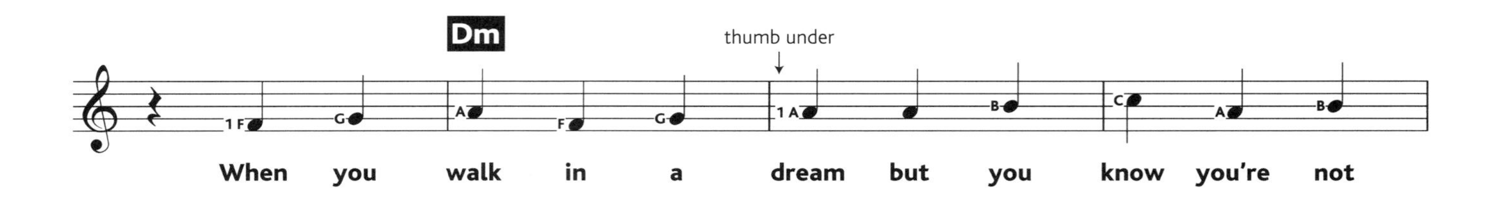
Dm
thumb under
1 F G A F G 1 A B C A B
When you walk in a dream but you know you're not

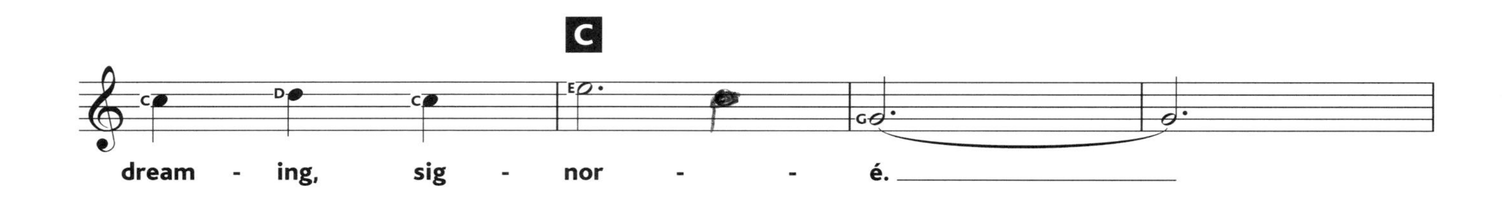
C
C D C E G
dream - ing, sig - nor - - é.

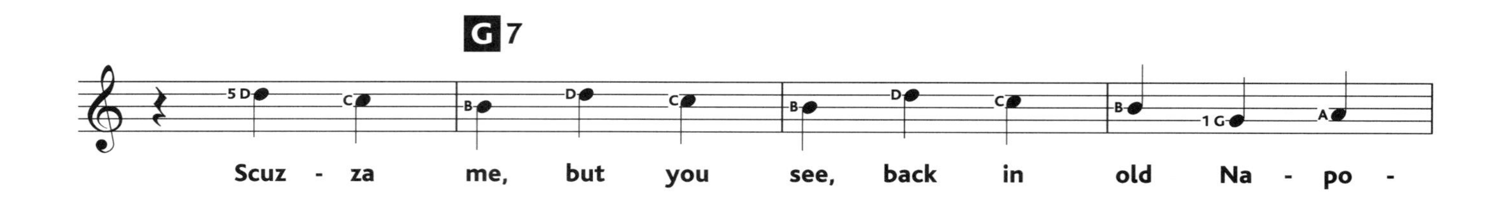
G7
5 D C B D C B D C B 1 G A
Scuz - za me, but you see, back in old Na - po -

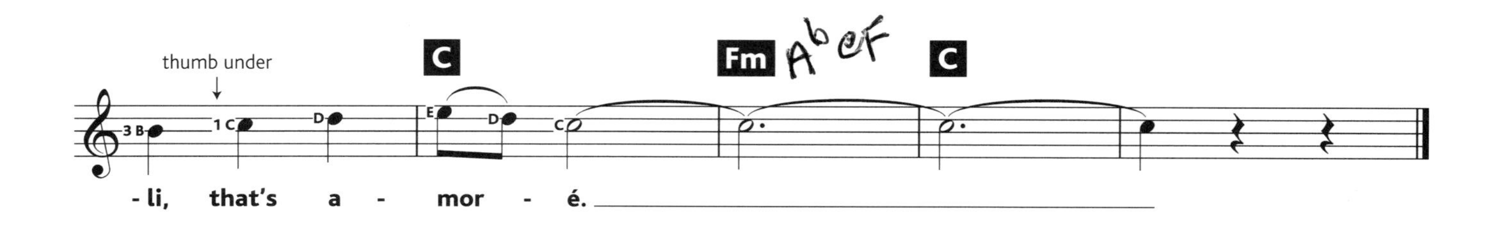
thumb under
C Fm C
3 B 1 C D E D C
- li, that's a - mor - é.

Walk On By

Words by Hal David
Music by Burt Bacharach

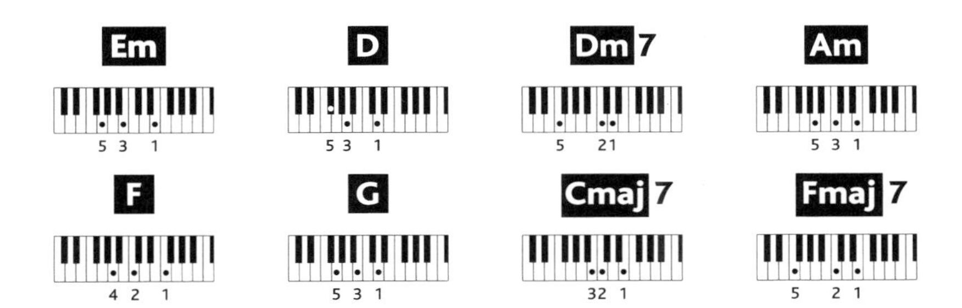
Em
5 3 1
D
5 3 1
Dm7
5 21
Am
5 3 1
F
4 2 1
G
5 3 1
Cmaj7
32 1
Fmaj7
5 2 1

Voice: **Flute**
Rhythm: **Bossa nova**
Tempo: **Moderately ♩ = 100**

Em
D
If you see me walk - ing down the street, and I start to cry
I just can't get ov - er los - ing you and if I seem

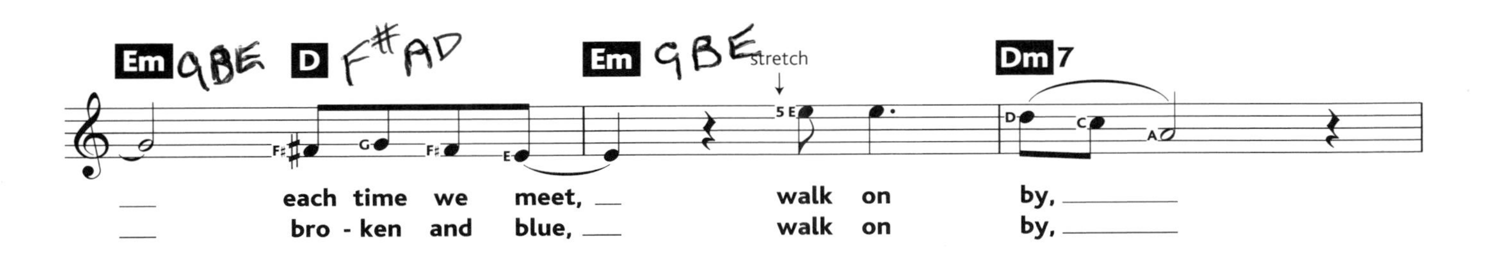
Em D Em Dm7
stretch
each time we meet, walk on by,
bro - ken and blue, walk on by,

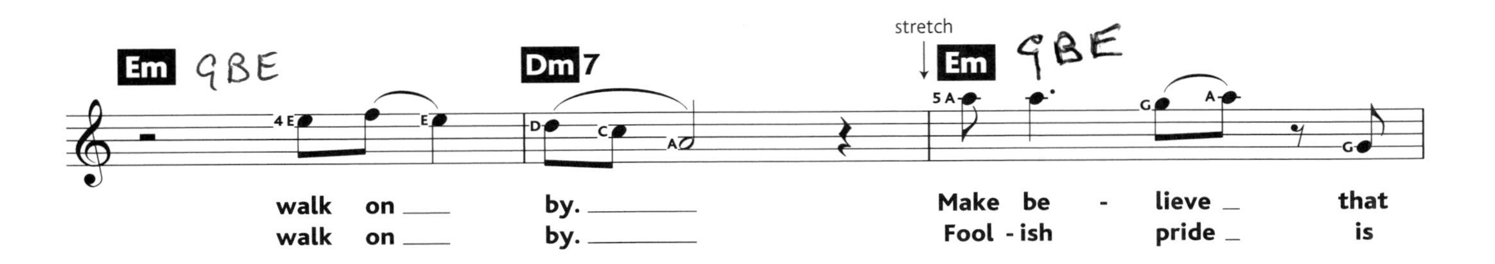
Em Dm7 Em
stretch
walk on by. Make be - lieve that
walk on by. Fool - ish pride is

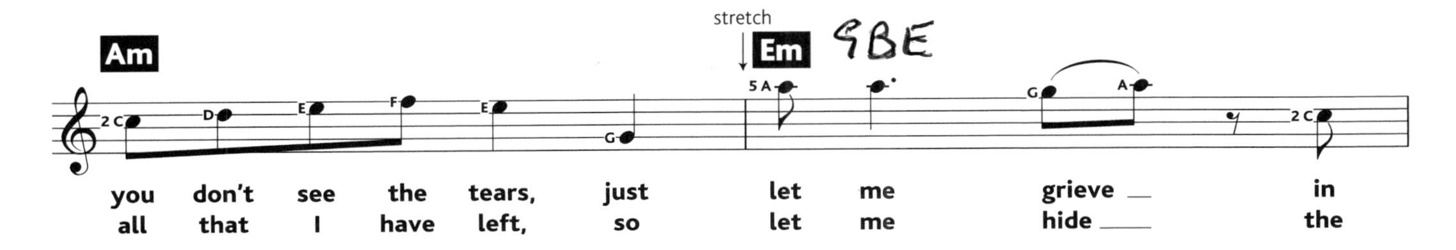
Am Em
stretch
you don't see the tears, just let me grieve in
all that I have left, so let me hide the

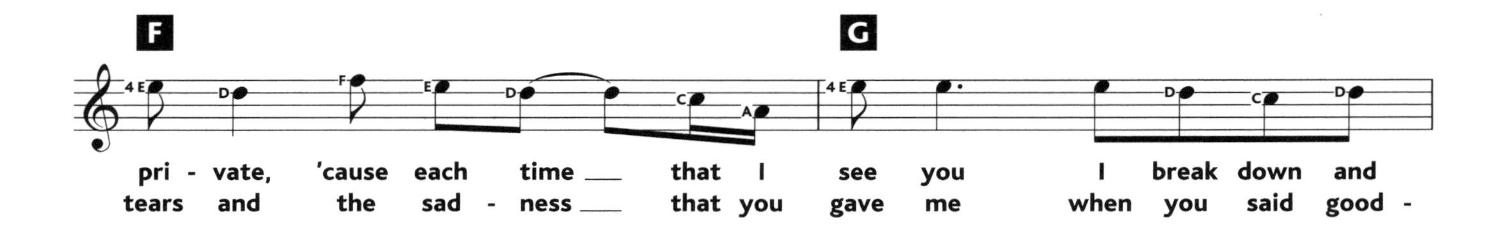
F
G
pri - vate, 'cause each time that I see you I break down and
tears and the sad - ness that you gave me when you said good -

Cmaj7 BCE
Fmaj7 FCE
Cmaj7 BCE
cry. Walk on by,
bye. you walked on by,

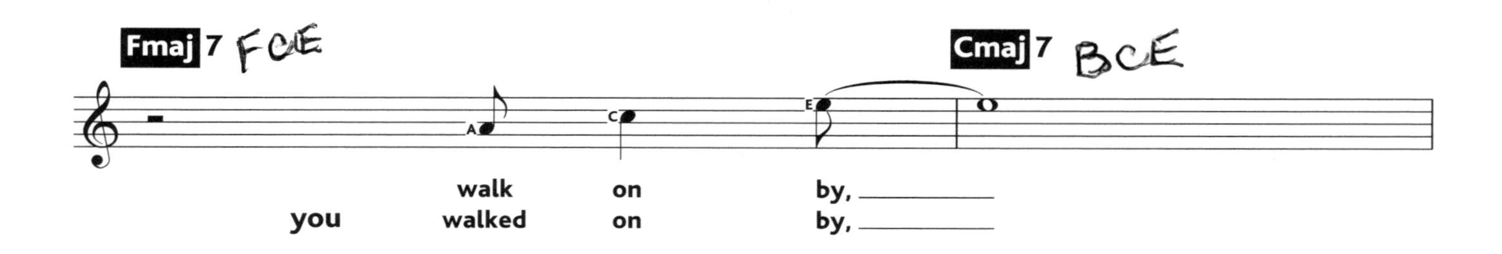
Fmaj7 FCE
Cmaj7 BCE
walk on by,
you walked on by,

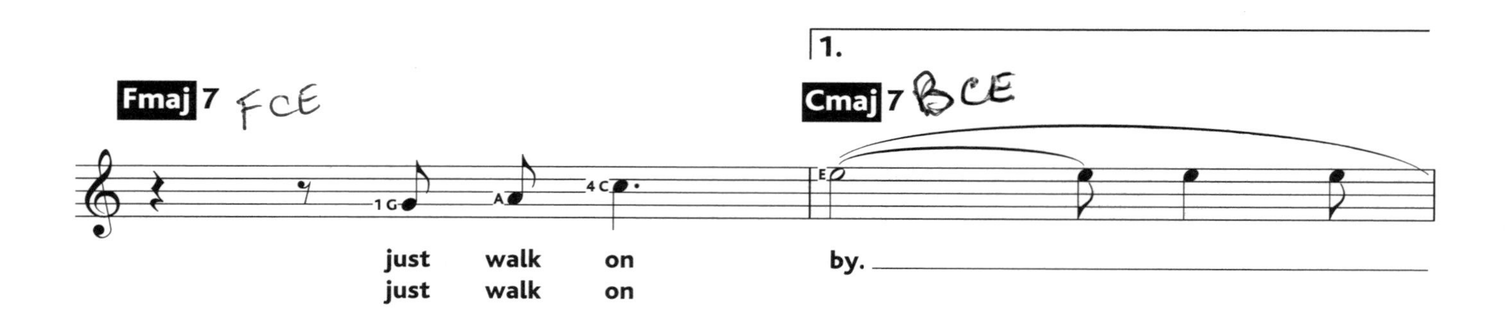
1.
Fmaj7 FCE
Cmaj7 BCE
just walk on by.
just walk on

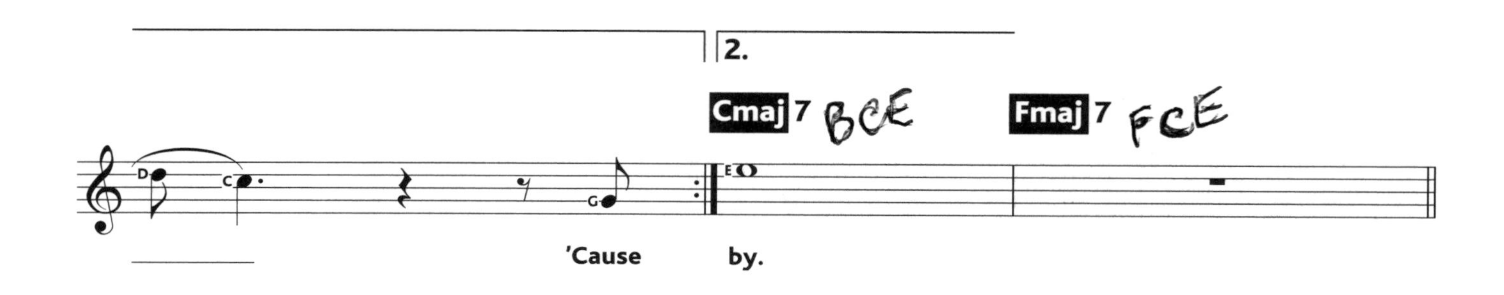
2.
Cmaj7 BCE
Fmaj7 FCE
'Cause by.

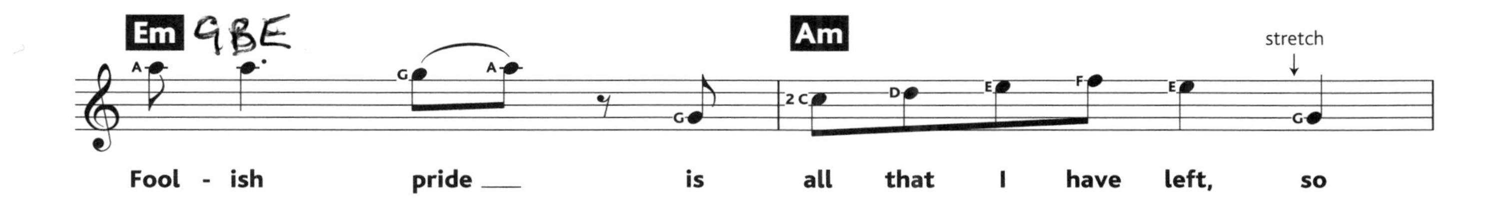
Em GBE
Am
stretch
Fool - ish pride ___ is all that I have left, so

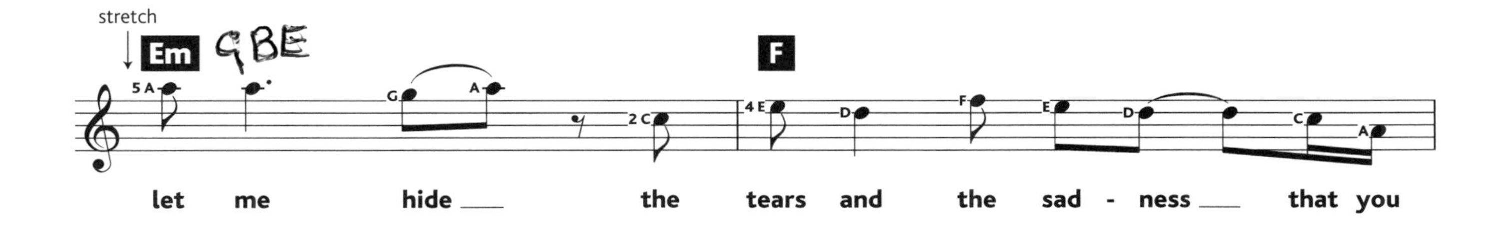
stretch
Em GBE
F
let me hide ___ the tears and the sad - ness ___ that you

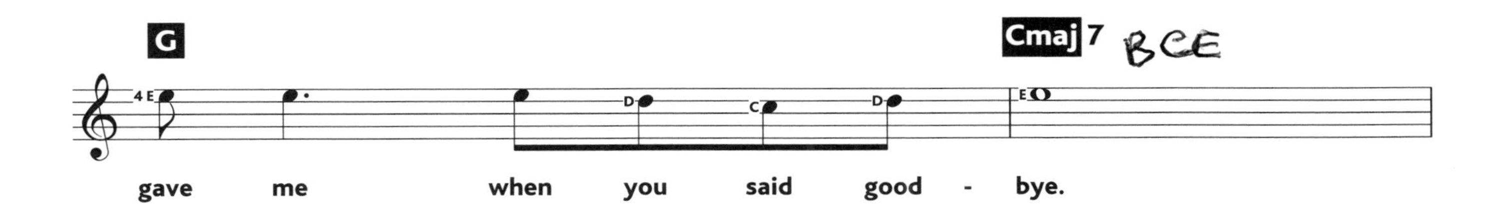
G
Cmaj7 BCE
gave me when you said good - bye.

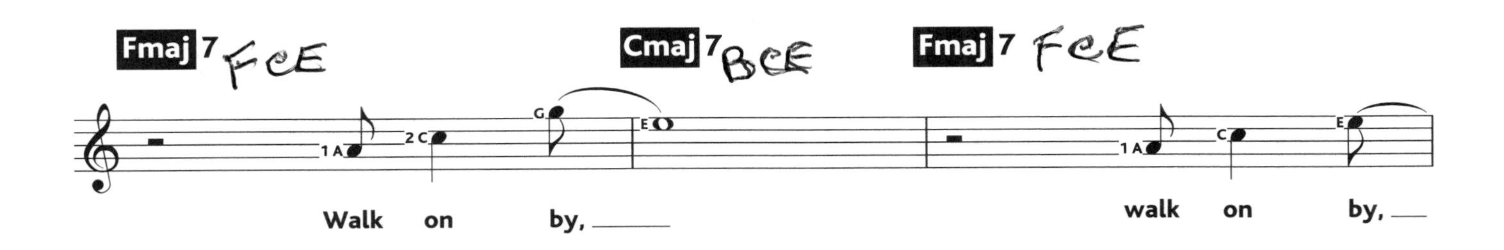
Fmaj7 FCE
Cmaj7 BCE
Fmaj7 FCE
Walk on by, ___ walk on by, ___

Cmaj7 BCE
Fmaj7 FCE
Cmaj7 BCE
just walk on

Wichita Lineman

Words & Music by Jimmy Webb

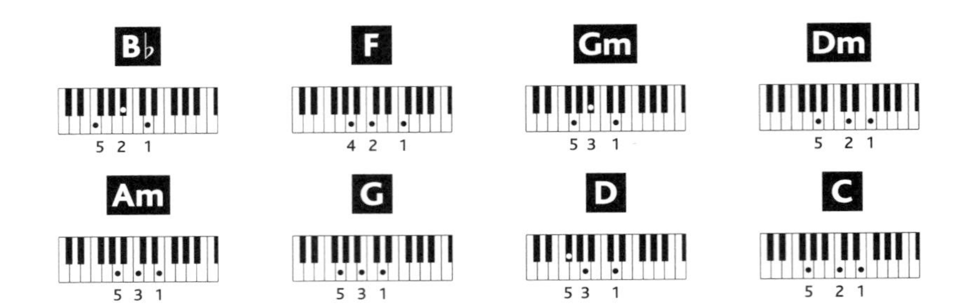

B♭
5 2 1
F
4 2 1
Gm
5 3 1
Dm
5 2 1
Am
5 3 1
G
5 3 1
D
5 3 1
C
5 2 1

Voice: **Electric guitar**
Rhythm: **Country**
Tempo: **Moderately ♩ = 100**

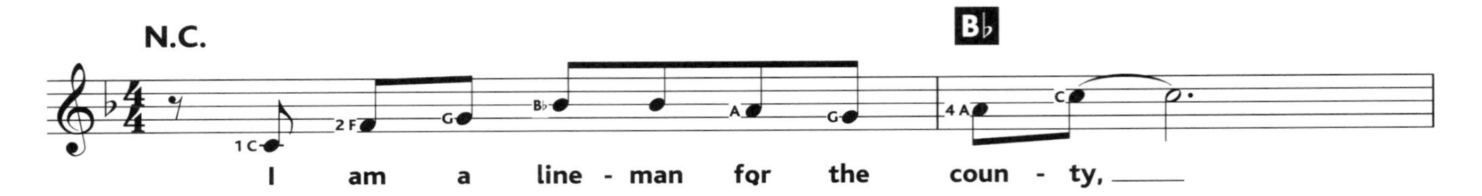

N.C.
B♭
I am a line - man for the coun - ty,

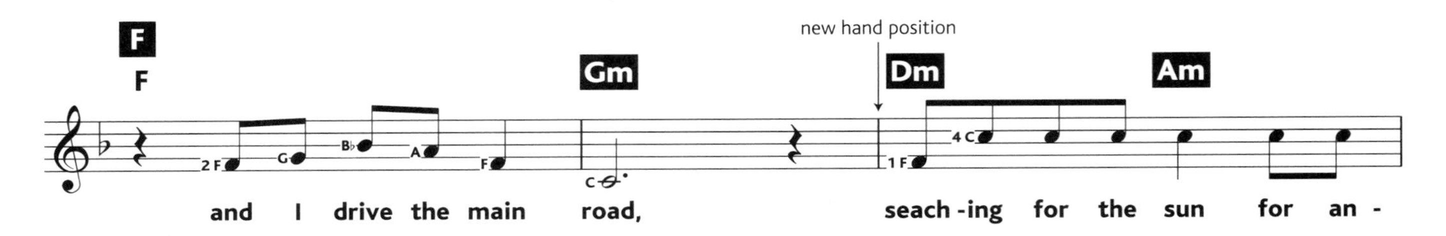

F
F
Gm
new hand position
Dm
Am
and I drive the main road, seach - ing for the sun for an -

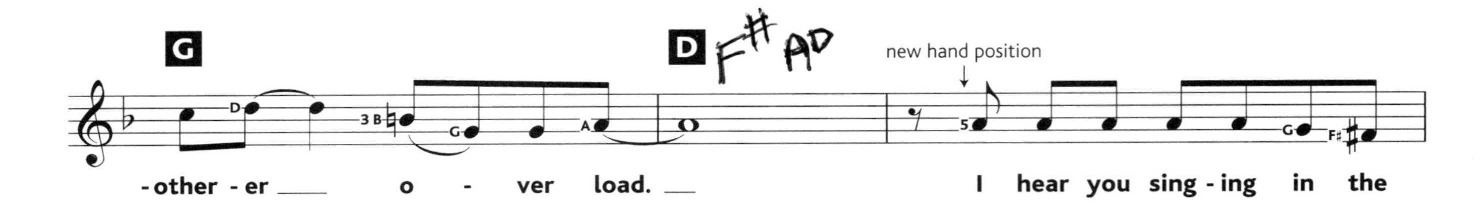

G
D
new hand position
- other - er o - ver load. I hear you sing - ing in the

C
G
wi - res, I can hear you through the whine,

Gm
D
Am
and the Wi - chi - ta Line - man is still on the

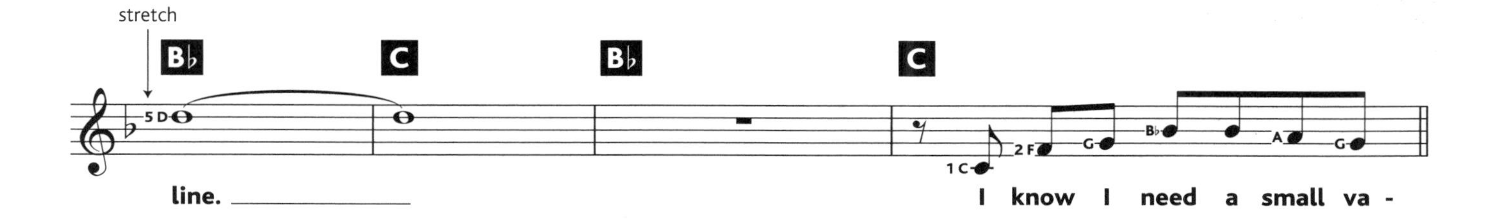
stretch
B♭ C B♭ C
5 D
1 C 2 F G B♭ A G
line. ______ I know I need a small va -

stretch
B♭ F Gm
new hand position
5 D A C
2 F G B♭ A F
C 1 F
- ca - tion, but it don't look like rain. And

Dm Am G D F#AD
4 C D 3 B♮ G A
if it snows, that stretch down south will nev - er ___ stand _ the strain. __

new hand position
C
5 G F♯ D E 5 A G F♯
And I need you more than want you, and I want you for all

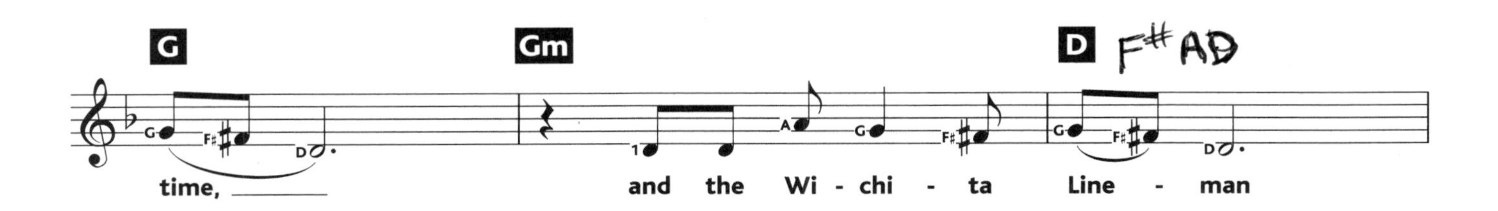
G Gm D F#AD
G F♯ D 1 A G F♯ G F♯ D
time, ______ and the Wi - chi - ta Line - man

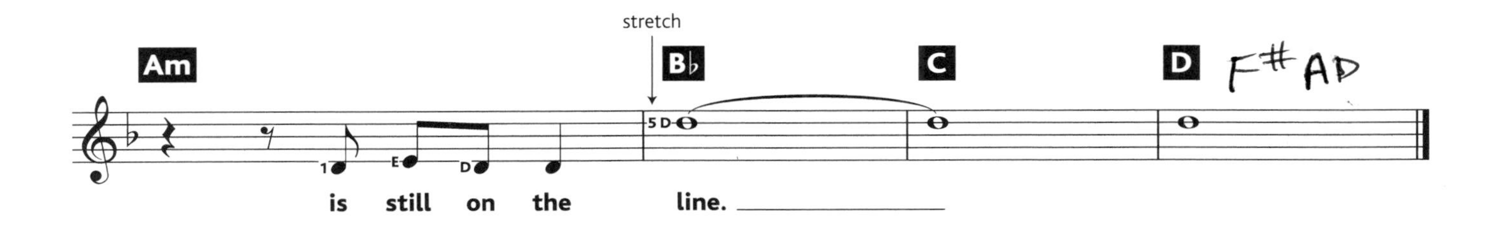
stretch
Am B♭ C D F#AD
1 E D 5 D
is still on the line. ______

What A Wonderful World

Words & Music by George Weiss & Bob Thiele

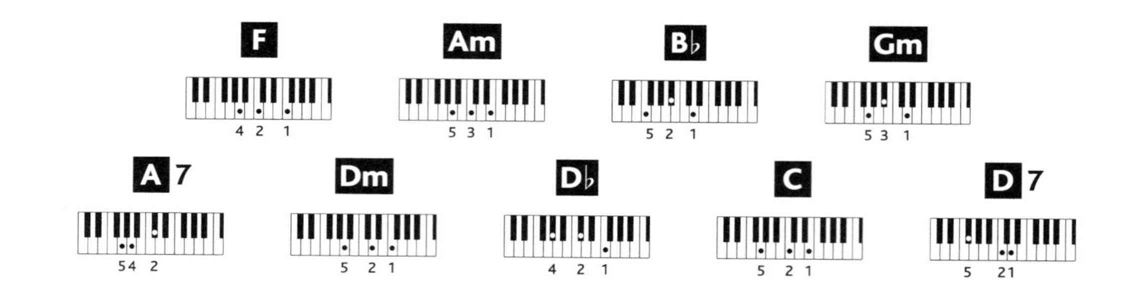

F
4 2 1
Am
5 3 1
B♭
5 2 1
Gm
5 3 1
A7
54 2
Dm
5 2 1
D♭
4 2 1
C
5 2 1
D7
5 21

Voice: **Clarinet**
Rhythm: **Swing**
Tempo: **Gently** ♩ **= 72**

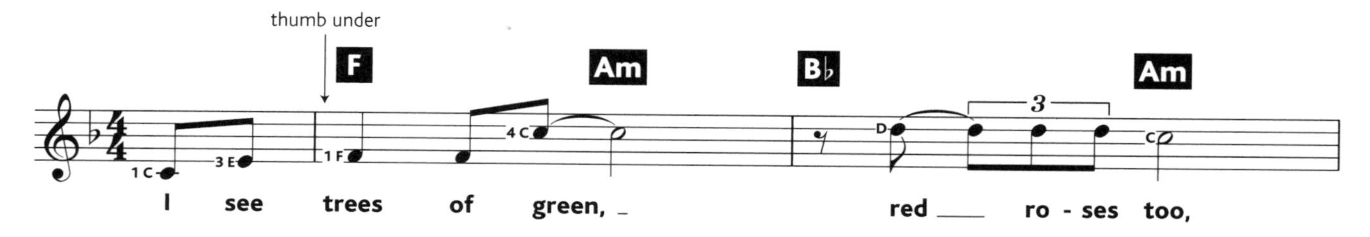

thumb under
F
Am
B♭
Am
3
I see trees of green, red ro - ses too,

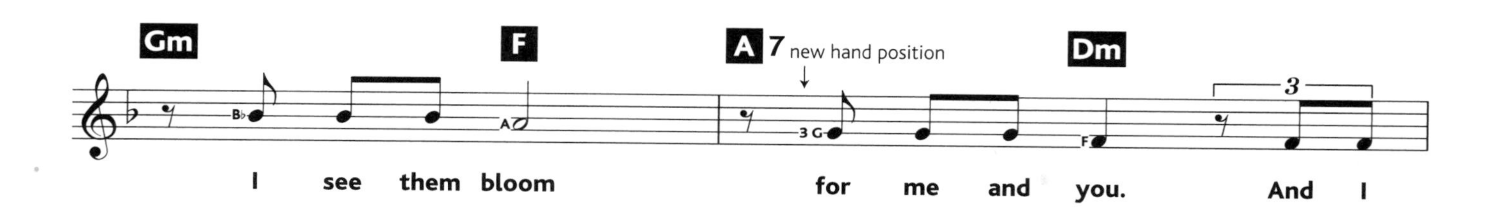

Gm
F
A7 new hand position
Dm
3
I see them bloom for me and you. And I

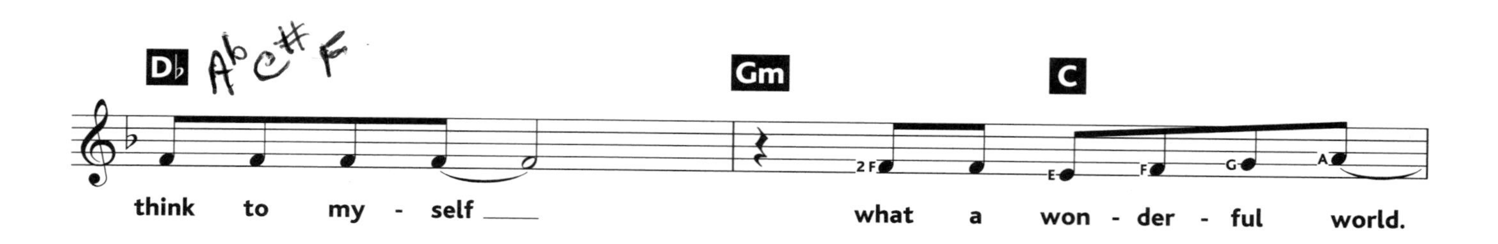

D♭
Gm
C
think to my - self what a won - der - ful world.

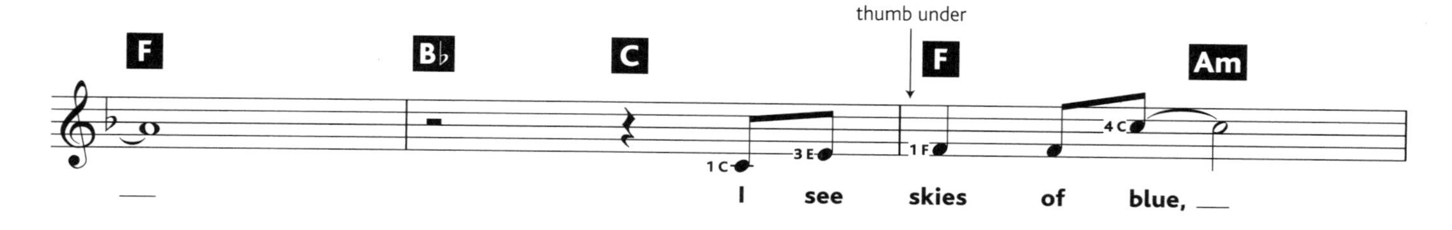

F
B♭
C
thumb under
F
Am
I see skies of blue,

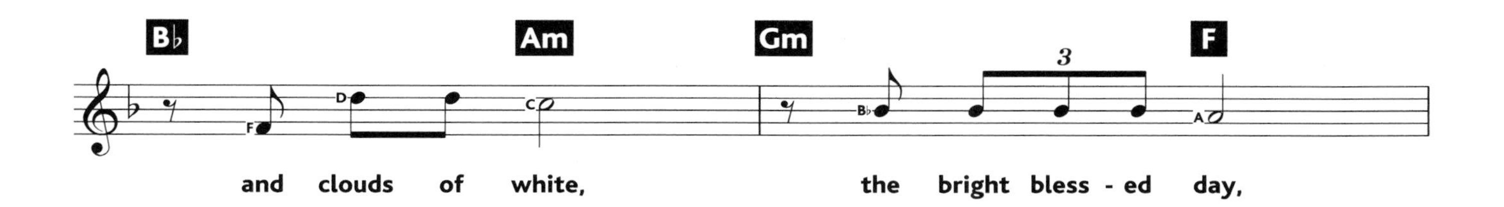
B♭ Am Gm F
3
and clouds of white, the bright bless - ed day,

A7 Dm D♭
A♭ C♯ F
3
the dark sa - cred night, and I think to my - self,

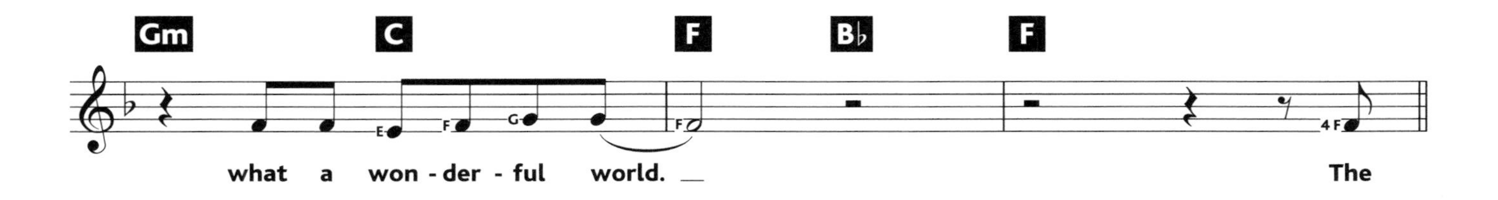
Gm C F B♭ F
what a won - der - ful world. The

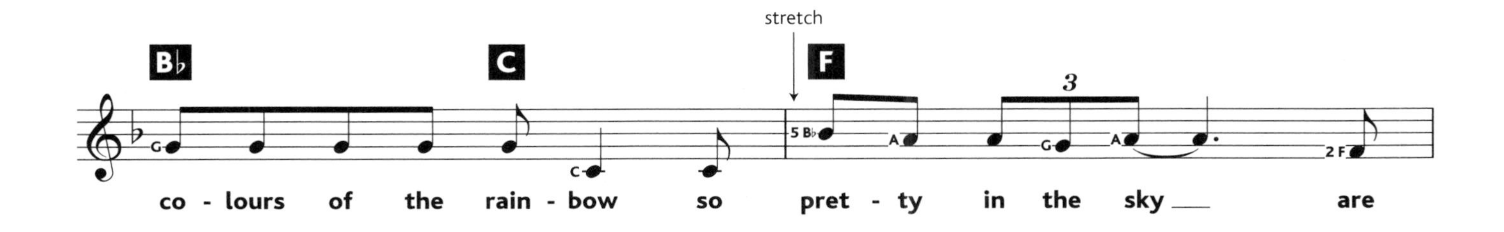
B♭ C F
stretch
3
co - lours of the rain - bow so pret - ty in the sky are

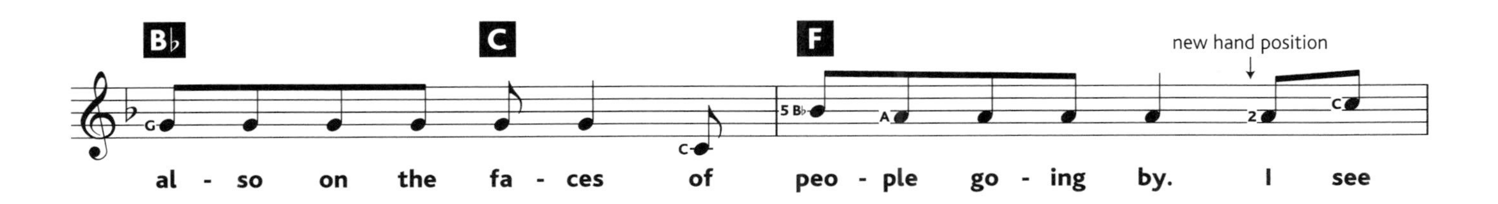
B♭ C F
new hand position
al - so on the fa - ces of peo - ple go - ing by. I see

Dm Am Dm Am
3
friends shak - ing hands, say - ing "How do you do?"

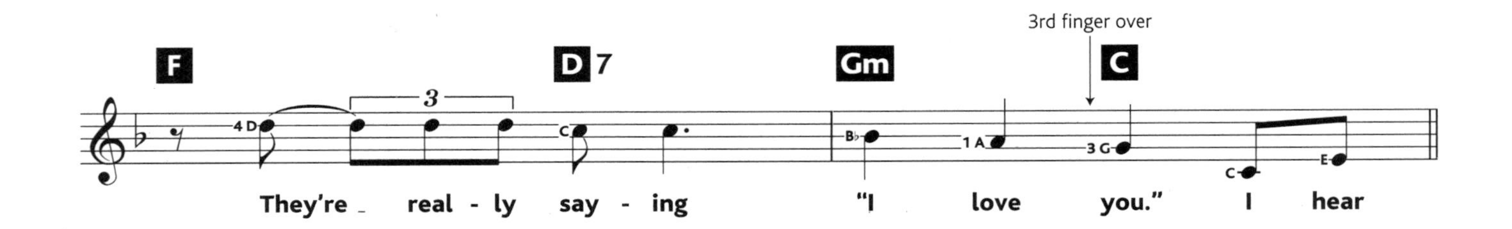
3rd finger over
F
D7
Gm
C
They're real - ly say - ing "I love you." I hear

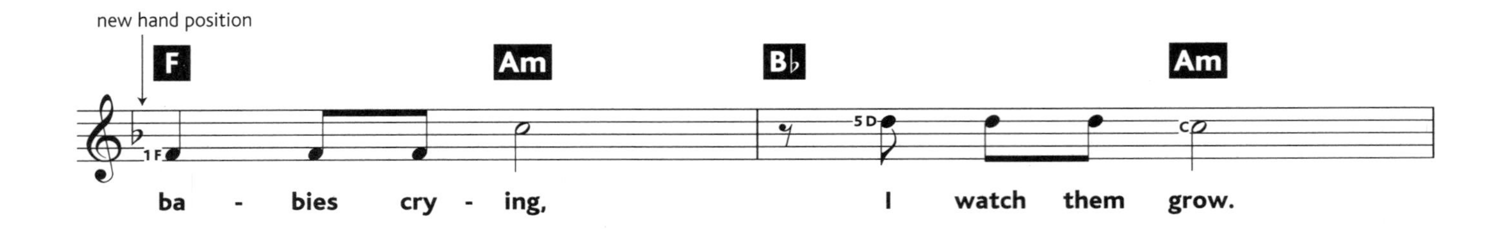
new hand position
F
Am
B♭
Am
ba - bies cry - ing, I watch them grow.

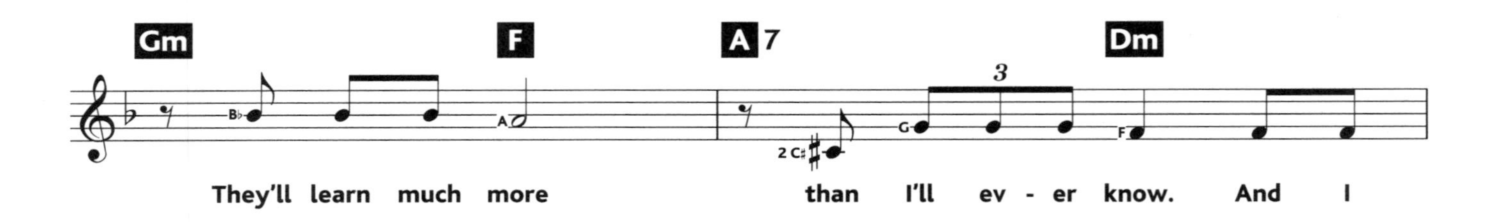
Gm
F
A7
Dm
They'll learn much more than I'll ev - er know. And I

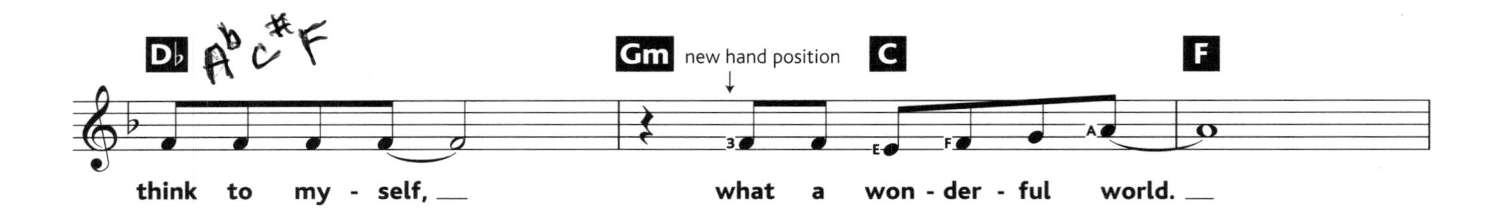
D♭
Gm
new hand position
C
F
think to my - self, what a won - der - ful world.

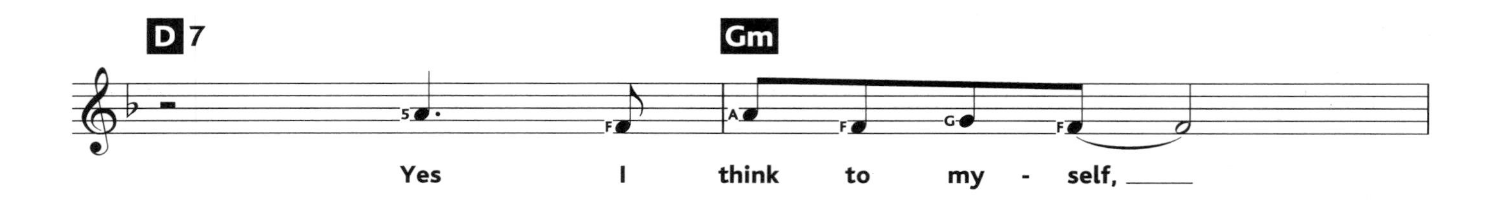
D7
Gm
Yes I think to my - self,

C
F
what a won - der - ful world.

1 2 3 4 5 6 7 8 9